Quest

English as a Second Language

Secondary Cycle Two
Year Three

Activity Book

Gillian Baxter
Cynthia Beyea
Claire Maria Ford

GRAFICOR
CHENELIÈRE ÉDUCATION

Quest
English as a Second Language
Secondary Cycle Two, Year Three

Activity Book

Gillian Baxter, Cynthia Beyea, Claire Maria Ford

© 2009 Chenelière Education Inc.

Editor: Susan Roy
Project managers: Angel Beyde, Jeanine Floyd
Proofreader: Joseph Shragge
Photo researcher: Rachel Irwin
Book designer and typesetter: Fenêtre sur cour
Printer: Imprimeries Transcontinental

Photos

Cover: (tl): Robert Kohlhuber/Istockphoto; **(tc):** Win Initiative/Getty Images; **(tr):** Mel Curtis/Getty Images; **(bl):** Private Collection/Ken Welsh/The Bridgeman Art Library; **(bc):** Courtesy NRC; **(br):** diego cervo/Istockphoto

Unit 1 p. 1: Mladen Mladenov/iStockphoto; **p. 2:** Superstock/Jupiter Images; **p. 4(t):** Arthur Kwiatkowski/iStockphoto; **(b):** HomeStudio/Shutterstock; **p. 5:** Ron Niebrugge/Mira.com; **p. 6:** Mazzzur/Shutterstock; **p. 7:** Hands Up; **p. 8:** Eric Isselée/iStockphoto; **p. 12:** Jennifer Stone/Shutterstock

Unit 2 p. 13: PhotoObjects.net/Jupiter Images; **p. 14:** mustafa deliormanli/iStockphoto; **p. 15:** Ana Blazic/iStockphoto; **p. 16:** Ericsphotography/iStockphoto; **p. 17:** William Casey/Shutterstock; **p. 18:** John Blair/Mira.com; **p. 19:** Rich Legg/iStockphoto; **p. 20:** Paul Austring Photography/Firstlight; **p. 24:** Jaimie Duplass/iStockphoto

Unit 3 p. 25: Corbis/Jupiter Images; **p. 27:** webphotographeer/iStockphoto; **p. 29:** Leigh Schindler/iStockphoto; **p. 30:** Ib Trebbien/iStockphoto; **p. 31:** Jamie Carroll/iStockphoto; **p. 35:** Big Cheese Photo/Jupiter Images; **p. 36:** Paul Pantazescu/iStockphoto

Unit 4 p. 37: Bomshtein/Shutterstock; **p. 38:** Monkey Business Images/Shutterstock; **p. 39:** Elke Dennis/Shutterstock; **p. 40:** Monkey Business Images/Shutterstock; **p. 43:** Gorin/Shutterstock; **p. 44:** Istockphoto; **p. 46:** coreay/iStockphoto; **p. 48:** Sideways Design/Shutterstock

Unit 5 p. 49: Cathleen Abers-Kimball/iStockphoto; **p. 50:** Peter Malsbury/iStockphoto; **p. 52:** Comstock/Jupiter images; **p. 54:** Micimakin/Shutterstock; **p. 55:** Courtesy Mathias Osvath; **p. 56:** © CellPress/courtesy Mathias Osvath; **p. 59:** Mikhail Grigoryev/Shutterstock

Unit 6 p. 61: Patrick Robert/Corbis; **p. 63:** RTimages/Alamy; **p. 64:** La Presse Canadienne/Kevin Frayer; **p. 66:** Tannis Toohey/GetStock.com; **p. 67:** WireImage/Getty Images; **p. 68:** Toronto Star/La Presse Canadienne(Steve Russell)

Unit 7 p. 73 (t): David Hughes/Shutterstock; **(b):** La Presse Canadienne/Everett Collection; **p. 74:** © Dean Conger/CORBIS; **p. 76:** Columbia/The Kobal Collection; **p. 77:** Peter Macdiarmid/Getty Images; **p. 78:** James Kingman/Shutterstock; **p. 79:** La Presse Canadienne/Lefteris Pitarakis; **p. 83:** James Kingman/Shutterstock

Unit 8 p. 87 (t): © Jenny E. Ross/Corbis; **(b):** UN Photo/Marco Dormino; **p. 89:** Nick C/iStockphoto; **p. 90:** Chris Whitehead/Getty Images; **p. 91:** John Kenney, © The Gazette Jan. 23, 2005; **p. 92:** Doug Allan/Getty Images; **p. 94:** © Kim Ludbrook/epa/Corbis

Unit 9 p. 98: Robert Churchill/iStockphoto; **p. 99:** Comstock/Jupiter images; **p. 100:** Big Cheese Photo/Jupiter images; **p. 101:** Benjamin Goode/iStockphoto; **p. 103:** Bertrand Benoit/Shutterstock; **p. 107:** Paul Mckeown/iStockphoto; **p. 108:** Rtimages/iStockphoto

Workshop 1 p. 112 (t): Image Source Black/Jupiter Images; **p. 113:** Thinkstock Images/Jupiter Images; **p. 114:** Ethan Myerson/iStockphoto; **p. 115:** © Novruzee/Dreamstime.com; **p. 116:** Helder Almeida/iStockphoto; **p. 117:** Izabela Habur/iStockphoto; **p. 119:** AbleStock/Jupiter Images; **p. 120:** Muharrem Öner/iStockphoto

Workshop 2 p. 122: Darko Novakovic/iStockphoto; **p. 123 (l):** Angela Hawkey/Shutterstock; **(c):** Alexander Hafemann/iStockphoto; **(r):** Mark Kostich/iStockphoto; **p. 124:** Don Hammond/Design Pics/Jupiter Images; **p. 126:** Wolfgang Steiner/iStockphoto; **p. 127:** Suzanne Tucker/Shutterstock; **p. 129:** Purestock/Jupiter Images

Workshop 3 p. 132: © Jean Dieuzaide/Rapho; **p. 133:** Yuri Arcurs/Shutterstock; **p. 134 (l):** © Bettmann/Corbis; **(r):** Jock McDonald Film; **p. 136:** Sgt Eric Jolin, Rideau Hall; **p. 138:** Sean Kilpatrick/Presse canadienne; **p. 143:** Chris Schmidt/iStockphoto

Reference Section p. 148: Susan Trigg/Istockphoto

Texts

Unit 4 p. 42-43: Used by permission from Battenfeld Group, LLC d/b/a MyFirstApartment.com

Unit 5 p. 55-56: «Hail From the Chimp: Zoo Ape Stockpiles Stones to Throw at Visitors» © CBC News [On line]-(March 13th, 2009)

Unit 7 p. 79-80: Gregory Katz, Shakespeare Portrait Unveiled © Associated Press-(March 9, 2009)

Unit 8 p. 91-92: Kevin Dougherty, A Senseless Slaughter, © The Gazette (Montreal)

Unit 9 p. 102-103: Terri L. Jones, Back to the Future © 2009 National Geographic Society. All rights reserved

GRAFICOR

CHENELIÈRE ÉDUCATION

7001 Saint-Laurent Blvd.
Montréal (Québec) Canada H2S 3E3
Telephone: 514 273-1066
Fax: 450 461-3834 / 1 888 460-3834
info@cheneliere.ca

ISBN 978-2-7652-1060-3

Dépôt légal: 2ᵉ trimestre 2009
Bibliothèque et Archives nationales du Québec
Bibliothèque et Archives Canada

Printed in Canada

2 3 4 5 ITIB 13 12 11 10

We acknowledge the financial support of the Government of Canada through the Book Publishing Industry Development Program (BPIDP) for our publishing activities.

Government of Quebec – Tax credit for book publishing – Administered by SODEC.

Member of the CERC

Member of the *Association nationale des éditeurs de livres*

CERC
Canadian Educational Resources Council

ASSOCIATION NATIONALE DES ÉDITEURS DE LIVRES

TABLE OF CONTENTS

Grammar

Direct and Indirect (Reported) Speech

Direct speech

You use **direct speech** to repeat the speaker's exact words. Use quotation marks to identify the words said and capitalize the first word that the speaker says.

Direct speech is introduced or followed by a verb explaining how the words are spoken, such as *say, complain, object, whisper, reply, shout.*

Indirect speech

You use **indirect speech** to report what someone says or writes without using the exact words. To do this, you must make certain changes.

Formation

* Change the tense of the speaker's original words one tense further into the past.
* Change pronouns and possessives as needed.
* Omit the comma and the quotation marks.
* Add the word *that* (optional).

Direct Speech	Indirect Speech
Simple present ⟶	**Simple past**
The woman told us, *"I accompany tour groups to Pompeii."*	*The woman told us (that) she accompanied tour groups to Pompeii.*
Present continuous ⟶	**Past continuous**
The woman told us, *"I am accompanying tour groups to Pompeii."*	*The woman told us (that) she was accompanying tour groups to Pompeii.*
Simple past ⟶	**Past perfect**
The woman told us, *"I accompanied tour groups to Pompeii."*	*The woman told us (that) she had accompanied tour groups to Pompeii.*
Future ⟶	**Present conditional**
The woman told us, *"I will accompany tour groups to Pompeii."*	*The woman told us (that) she would accompany tour groups to Pompeii.*

→ LEARN MORE

To use indirect speech to report an information question, you will also need to:
- change the verb *said* to *asked*
- change the interrogative form of the verb to the affirmative form
- replace the question mark with a period

To report a yes/no question, add the word *if* or *whether*.

Direct Speech	Indirect Speech
Interrogative ⟶	Affirmative
Natalya **said**, "Where are you going next?" Claudio **said**, "Are you going to Buenos Aires?"	Natalya **asked** where I was going next. Claudio **asked whether** I was going to Buenos Aires.

Frequent Errors

Practise your editing skills. Read the sentences and circle the error in the use of indirect speech. Write the corrected sentence below each example.

1. They told us that they will meet us at the plaza.

_____

2. Olivier said than he was leaving for Cairo on Saturday night.

_____

3. She said that, she would come to the hotel after skiing.

_____

4. Carlos and Jen asked Tim if he would bring his snowboard?

_____

5. The pilot said that "we were travelling at an altitude of 15 000 metres."

_____

Practise 1

Change the reported speech to direct speech.

1. They reported that it had been an amazing trip and that everything had been perfect.

_____

_____

2. Then Ben complained that the airline company had lost his luggage.

_____

3. Samara added that she had lost her shopping bag in the Paris Métro.

_____

4. Annie answered that that was true.

_____

5. Yazid pointed out that they had got Ben's suitcase anyhow.

_____

6. Ben retorted that it had been found the day before their flight, and that that hadn't helped much.

_____

7. Samara commented sadly that she had lost her shopping bag forever.

_____

8. Mélina yelled for everyone to look at what she had found in her stuff.

_____

9. Everyone said in chorus that it was Samara's shopping bag.

_____

10. I concluded that all was well that ended well.

_____

Practise 2

Change the following sentences to reported speech.

1. The pilot announced, "We are beginning our descent to Barcelona."

_____

2. The tour guide stated, "We will meet in the lobby for dinner at 6:00 p.m."

_____

3. All the travel blog reviews claimed, "Hotel Paradiso is a dump!"

_____

4. "It is taking so long to get my new passport!" I complained.

_____

5. "The Giraldilla was built in the 12th century," the pamphlet informed us.

_____

Your Turn

Write a short text about a conversation with a friend in which you talked about a difficult situation during a trip. Use direct speech and indirect speech at least twice, with correct punctuation.

_____

_____

_____

_____

_____

Interrogative Form

Information Questions

To ask an **information question**, start with the question word, followed by the auxiliary, subject, main verb and the rest of the sentence. The auxiliary and the form of the main verb will depend on the tense.

Question words include interrogative pronouns (*who, what, which, whose*), adjectives (*what, which, whose*) and adverbs (*where, when, why, how*).

To Ask About	Question Word	Examples
Identity of persons, things or events	Who*	*Who will you visit in New York?*
	What *	*What did you plan to do?*
	Which	*Which way is the Empire State Building?*
Possession	Whose	*Whose backpack is this?*
Place	Where	*Where has he left the map?*
Time	When	*When will you get the pictures developed?*
Reason	Why	*Why do we have to wait here?*
Means, manner, degree	How	*How can I find out where the bus stops?* *How well does she know the city?*

* When *who* or *what* is the subject, use the affirmative form of the verb instead of the interrogative: *Who **bought** the tickets? What **happens** next?*

Yes/No Questions

To ask a **yes/no question**, start with the auxiliary verb, followed by the subject, base form of the main verb and the rest of the sentence. The form of the auxiliary will depend on the tense.

*Jodie **took** the train to New York.* ➔ *Did Jodie **take** the train to New York?*

For the verb *to be*, invert the verb and the subject.

*The Empire State Building **is** in Manhattan.* ➔ *Is the Empire State Building in Manhattan?*

Frequent Errors

Read an interview with a student who is spending three months in Mexico with her family. The error in each sentence is highlighted: correct it.

1. ReQuest Radio: Hello Caroline. When you leave for Mexico with your family?

   _____

   Caroline: We left on January 4th.

2. ReQuest: How they travel?

   _____

   Caroline: We went by camper. We have a huge Winnebago.

3. ReQuest: Everyone sleep in the camper?

   _____

   Caroline: Yes, my little sister and I, and my parents.

4. ReQuest: What you do about school?

   _____

   Caroline: My mom home-schools us and we email and chat with our teachers.

5. ReQuest: Miss your friends?

   _____

   Caroline: For sure! But we chat with them too!

6. ReQuest: Today what doing you?

   _____

   Caroline: We're going to the beach! It's hot and sunny. *Hasta luego!*

Practise 1

Change the sentences into questions. Use the words in bold to guide your choice.

1. Yes, the travel magazine **has articles in English and French.**

   _____

2. The first ad features **a two-page spread about Cape Town.**

   _____

3. **Pierre Hatfield** wrote the article on ecotourism in Tasmania.

   _____

4. People travel **to discover new cultures, historical places and beautiful scenery.**

_____

5. Akim particularly enjoyed **the article about Seville.**

_____

6. The ad for the Colorado snowboarding holiday is **toward the end.**

_____

7. **Yes**, the airline supports ecotourism in its magazine.

_____

Practise 2

Read the text and write two yes/no questions and two information questions about the Chinese language. Write the answers to the questions.

Chinese is a pictorial language. Every word is a different picture and has to be memorized separately. There is no alphabet and no connection between the written and spoken language. A person can learn to read and write Chinese without knowing how to speak one word. Because each word is a pictograph, Chinese calligraphy evokes a greater emotional response than the same word lettered in alphabet. The art of calligraphy is highly revered in China. Poetry written in calligraphy by ancient masters is prized and passed on from generation to generation.

Source: *Chinese Cinderella: The True Story of an Unwanted Daughter*, Adeline Yen Mah.

Yes/No questions:

1. _____

_____

2. _____

_____

Information questions:

1. _____

_____

2. _____

_____

Your Turn

Think of a trip that students from your school have already taken. You want to write an article for your school newspaper; prepare five interview questions to ask your classmates.

1. _____

2. _____

3. _____

4. _____

5. _____

Read and Respond

TRAVEL & TOURISM

Voluntouring: For Them or for Me?

This month, our journalist explores the controversial nature of this do-good trend.

By Sandra Wong

Voluntouring has become a popular travel trend that enables tourists of all ages to combine travel with volunteering. There are two types of projects: humanitarian, such as teaching, giving medical aid or building homes, and environmental. Examples of environmental projects are tracking wildlife, saving turtle populations, and surveying reefs. But did you know that voluntouring is controversial? What do you think? Read on and decide for yourself.

Experts on the topic declare that often it is nothing more than a form of voyeurism: watching people suffer, knowing full well that participants will come back to their own comfort zone in a few short days. On a recent radio show in Sherbrooke, callers complained that tourists are not really skilled to deal with the problems they encounter. One university student even declared angrily, "They return home with nothing more than reinforced prejudices about developing countries!" Another caller said that voluntouring is an option only open to the rich in our society, since trips typically cost over $1500.

However, this is not everyone's opinion. As Gilles Berthier, a Gatineau teacher who took a group of students to Honduras, commented, "Students often begin **fundraisers** two years before leaving. That takes a lot of time and energy and proves that if you're motivated, you can find a way." Another school, from Repentigny, had an opportunity to **pitch in** when they went to rural Peru to work in an orphanage while learning about the local culture and seeing the country's attractions. Fatima, 17, a student who went to Peru, **touts** the benefits of helping the less fortunate. She says she has a clearer vision of the world's challenges. Hugo, 16, who also went, said the people's resilience **in spite of** difficult living conditions impressed him.

You don't always have to board a plane to do voluntourism. Domestic projects involve cleaning up provincial parks or restoring communities after natural disasters. Tim Dewitt, who heads up a provincial park project, claims, "Local projects are a fantastic way to let teens see a new part of the province, and learn more about themselves and environmental issues."

Whether overseas or at home, participants return **thrilled** with the way they were able to help others. They enthusiastically describe it as a rewarding experience and an education. It opens their horizons to see how locals remain optimistic in the face of extreme poverty or tragic violence. Participants say that they learn a lot about culture, people and the world in a **hands-on** way. As Laurianne, 18, commented, "Helping the turtles of Mexico made me want to study zoology next year. I want to learn more, so I can help more!"

"The bottom line," concludes Lise Després, a voluntourism organization president, "is that the project be carried out with respect for both participants and locals. There needs to be training, one-on-one contact and tangible results. When these conditions are met, everyone benefits!"

Explore the Text

Before Reading

1. Look at the title and the photos on pages 7 and 8 and write three key words that summarize what you think this article will be about.

_____ _____ _____

2. What arguments do you think could be made against voluntourism?

_____

_____

3. Locate the vocabulary words (listed in the left column below), in the text on pages 7 and 8. Read the sentence in which each word appears. Then match the words with their synonyms in the right column. Use your dictionary.

a) fundraiser _____   **1.** animals

b) tout _____   **2.** excited

c) pitch in _____   **3.** way to make money

d) wildlife _____   **4.** help, get busy

e) thrilled _____   **5.** talk positively about

4. Use four of the above words in sentences to demonstrate your understanding.

_____

_____

_____

_____

While Reading

5. As you read the article, underline the arguments for voluntourism (the pros) and circle the arguments against voluntourism (the cons) in the text.

After Reading

6. Read the following statements about voluntourism. Circle **T** if the text confirms the statement, and **F** if the text refutes the statement. Write the number of the paragraph where you find the answer beside the statement.

a) Voluntourism eradicates prejudices. _____	T	F
b) There are two types of voluntourism: humanitarian and environmental. _____	T	F
c) Voluntourism is too expensive for students. _____	T	F
d) An effective voluntourist project does not require any training for the participants. _____	T	F
e) Voluntourism may help young people decide on a career. _____	T	F

7. How does Mr. Berthier refute the claim that voluntourism is only for the rich?

_____

_____

_____

8. Reread the text to fill in the inverted triangle.

Headline: _____

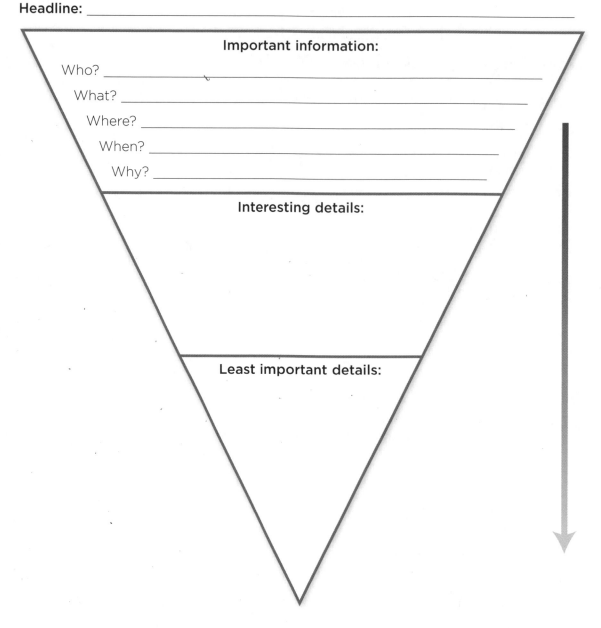

Important information:

Who? _____

What? _____

Where? _____

When? _____

Why? _____

Interesting details:

Least important details:

Connect With the Text

9. The university student said, "They [voluntourists] return home with nothing more than reinforced prejudices about developing countries." How do you think this occurs? Come up with an example to support your answer.

_____

_____

_____

_____

_____

10. What suggestions would you make to improve the voluntourist experience?
Identify and describe two problems and provide solutions.

_____

_____

_____

_____

_____

_____

11. Do you think you would make a good voluntourist candidate? Explain how with
examples and illustrations.

_____

_____

_____

_____

_____

Generalize

12. Review the pros and cons you underlined or circled in the text. Write an article to
express your opinion on voluntourism. Integrate ideas from the text to support
your ideas. Remember to follow the inverted triangle model. Conclude by stating
whose arguments are stronger: the participants' or the critics'.

I'm for the voluntouring because, personnaly, I
want to try it one day. I've the same opinion
than the two teachers; these travels make
learn to students what is the reality in
less developing country, we learn to
help other people, we learn to make
something real and important. I can
understand people who doesn't approve it like
the experts in the topic and some people who
call at the sherbrook show radio but I think
they just never try it and they are scared
by the thing they doesn't know.

_____

Vocabulary

Practise

Circle the word that doesn't belong with the others on each line. Use your dictionary.

Word	Outsider		
1. gruelling	easy	strenuous	exhausting
2. rugged	rough	smooth	harsh
3. keen	excited	interested	bored
4. awareness	knowledge	ignorance	consciousness
5. trek	journey	hike	rest

Learn More

Match each definition below with a word from the word bank. Use your dictionary.

Word Bank		
• backpacking	• hitchhike	• sightseeing
• currency	• landmark	• tour guide
• exchange	• off the beaten track	• trend
• fare	• road trip	

1. Away from towns: _____

2. Money: _____

3. Journey by car: _____

4. To get free rides in strangers' cars: _____

5. Price paid to travel: _____

Your Turn

Choose three words from the word bank that you <u>did not</u> match. Write a short blog entry using these words to describe a trip you took with your friends or family.

_____

_____

_____

_____

Grammar

Modal Auxiliaries

You use **modal auxiliaries** (*can, could, may, might, must, will, would, shall, should*), to express ability, intention, obligation, advice, permission, possibility or request.

Modal	To Express	Example
can	ability	*Can Deepak catch up on his math?*
could	possibility	*He could find a book on meditation in the library.*
	advice	*You could ask the doctor about the symptoms.*
	past ability	*When Tara was a competitive swimmer, she could swim three hours a day.*
	request	*Could you help us find a solution to this dilemma, please?*
may	permission	*You may leave the clinic in 15 minutes.*
	possibility	*Tariq may take a telephone counselling course this spring.*
might	lesser possibility	*If Manon tries hard, she might win.*
must	obligation	*We must deal with the negativism in the group.*
	advice	*You really must talk to her about how she got over the loss.*
will	definite intention	*You will feel much better once you have made your decision.*
would	request	*Would you send her a sympathy card, please?*
shall	request for advice or agreement	*Shall we go to see Ali play in the wheelchair tournament?*
should	advice	*We should try to look at it from a different angle.*
	strong possibility	*If Joe gets counselling, he should feel better.*

Formation

Negative: Add *not* after the modal.

*Paul could**n't** take the exam. He might **not** graduate on time.*

Interrogative: Start with the modal auxiliary, followed by the subject and the base form of the main verb.

Could acupuncture help with depression?
Would they like to try yoga?

Name: _____ Date: _____ Group: _____

Frequent Errors

Read the sentences and find the errors. Use the rule to help you correct the sentences.

1. *Suzy thinks the virus infect many people.*

Rule: Modals are verbs that are used before a main verb.

Correction: _____

2. *You shoud talk to the teacher if you don't understand.*

Rule: *Should* (like *could* and *would*) takes an *l*.

Correction: _____

3. *Ludovic should go not to the doctor this afternoon.*

Rule: To express the negative form of modals, add *not* between the modal and the main verb.

Correction: _____

4. *Where the first aid kit could be?*

Rule: To form an information question, follow this pattern: Question word + modal + subject + main verb + rest of sentence.

Correction: _____

5. *Will come Dr. Patel to the clinic today?*

Rule: To form a yes/no question, follow this pattern: Modal + subject + main verb + rest of sentence.

Correction: _____

Practise 1

Choose the most appropriate modal to complete the sentences. Then, use the underlined words in the sentence to write a question using the modal.

1. Mikael _____ (*would/should*) see Dr. Patel <u>Wednesday</u> at the latest.

_____

2. Families of patients _____ (*must/may*) <u>check in with the nursing station</u> before visiting.

_____

3. The hockey player _____ (*must/could*) be out <u>for the rest of the season</u> because of her injury.

_____

Reproduction prohibited © Chenelière Education inc.

4. Zac _____ (could/might) <u>not make the team</u> if he doesn't participate in the competition.

_____

5. The YMCA has changed the time for teen yoga so now we _____ (can/shall) <u>make it there on time</u> after class.

_____

Practise 2

Read the email to ReQuest Teen Helpline. Write two possible answers for each question using the suggested modal. Use the affirmative form in one answer and the negative in the second.

To: ReQuest Teen Helpline
From: Dizzy guy
Subject: SOS!

Dear ReQuest Helpline,

Can you help me? I am in my last year of high school and term one is just about done. Next year I want to go into Human Sciences, so my marks are super important. I think I am failing math. I have never had problems before, but this year is awful. I don't know what's going on! I have so much homework this year. I am the class president and I am on the yearbook committee and the trip committee. I also work part-time at a clothing store. I am so busy! What should I do? I feel like everything is spinning out of control!

Ken

1. What is Ken's problem? (Use *may/might*)

_____

2. What are two resources Ken could refer to for help? (Use *could*)

_____

_____

3. What advice would you give? (Use *should*)

_____

_____

4. What might happen if things don't change? (Use *might*)

_____

_____

5. What would you do if you were Ken? (Use *would*)

_____

_____

6. How do you suggest he start to change? (Use *can*)

_____

_____

_____

Your Turn

Read the story starter. Use three of the five suggestions below to continue the story.

Luisa couldn't wait to get home. She had just bought a new video game at lunchtime and wanted to try it out. As she came around the corner of the school, she heard a boy shouting, "Hey, give that back to me!" Luisa noticed a taller student push the boy to the ground and take off running with the boy's knapsack in his hand. For a brief second, Luisa didn't know what to do . . .

Suggestions
• What Luisa *could/couldn't* do. • What she *can/cannot* do.
• What Luisa *should/shouldn't* do. • What Luisa finally did!
• What she *might* do.

_____

_____

_____

_____

_____

_____

_____

_____

_____

Sentence Structure Using Conjunctions

A sentence may contain one or more clauses. Sentences can be divided into three basic structures: simple, compound and complex.

- **Simple** sentences contain one main clause.

  The adolescent (subject) *recovered* (verb).

- **Compound** sentences contain two or more main clauses, usually connected by a **coordinating conjunction**. The most common coordinating conjunctions are: *and, but, or, nor, yet, so.*

Sentence 1:	*The doctor examined Hal.* (simple sentence)
Sentence 2:	*She took X-rays.* (simple sentence)
Compound sentence:	*The doctor examined Hal and she took X-rays.*

- **Complex** sentences contain at least one main clause and one subordinate clause, usually connected by a **subordinating conjunction**. The most common subordinating conjunctions are: *after, although, as, because, before, how, if, once, than, that, though, unless, until, when, where, whether, while.*

Main clause:	*Yasmin was on the ski lift . . .*
Subordinate clause:	*when she fell . . .*
Complex sentence:	*Yasmin was on the ski lift when she fell.*

  The bus driver was in shock after he suddenly skidded out of control on the black ice. He didn't know whether anyone was injured.

  The parents were worried because their children hadn't arrived on time.

  The police did not contact the school until the report had been filled out.

  Everyone was relieved once they got the news.

Frequent Errors

Correct the sentence construction errors in the following sentences.

1. When people are depressed they may overspend. Or they overeat.

   _____

2. Sometimes problems seem so big there is always a solution.

   _____

3. It's important to stay active you're going through a hard time.

   _____

4. Because teens feel powerless. They often isolate themselves.

_____

5. I started to feel better. Once I told my mother what had happened.

_____

6. I often talk to my parents sometimes I just talk to my friends.

_____

Practise 1

Identify the structure of each of the sentences. Write *simple, compound* or *complex,* then circle the conjunction and say whether it is subordinating (*sub*) or coordinating (*coor*).

1. Things are great until one day "BANG," the friendship is over. _____

2. You used to do everything together! _____

3. How do you deal with the fallout? _____

4. The first thing is to keep your chin up and stay active. _____

5. Remember the good times but don't forget the bad times. _____

6. You'll start feeling better when you realize you'll make new friends soon. _____

Practise 2

Write logical compound or complex sentences by combining the ideas with conjunctions.

1. Marc and Laila had a car accident – they went off the road because of the fog.

_____

_____

2. Marc and Laila got out safely – their car was a wreck.

_____

_____

3. The ambulance and police did not leave – the teens said they were okay.

_____

_____

4. Everyone talked about the accident at school – it was in the local news.

_____

_____

5. The teens enjoyed the attention – they wouldn't want it to happen again.

_____

_____

6. Marc was not sure – he wanted to drive again – he knew he had to try.

_____

_____

Your Turn

Complete the text with the appropriate conjunctions: *and, but, unless, although, because, at least, so, however, or.*

Sure, life is not always easy, _____ you can always find a different way of looking at your situation. Looking at the flip side helps you see things differently _____ find a way to have a great day.

Key One: Look around you. You are not alone _____ you may feel that way. People are there who can help you. Never be afraid to ask.

Key Two: Choose. Will you blame _____ complain, _____ will you be thankful for what's going right? Write a list of positive facts about your situation.

Key Three: Tap that power. How can you know how resilient you are _____ you put yourself in a situation where you have to use your strength? You're getting stronger!

Key Four: Focus. Take the time to sit down _____ set your priorities. _____ the mountain may appear huge, focus on what's important now and take one baby step at a time.

Key Five: Relax and laugh. If nothing else works, _____ there's always laughter that can help. Go see a good comedy! Hey . . . have a great day!

Read and Respond

One Hoop at a Time: David's Story

I was 16 at the time. I stopped taking the school bus the day my best friend Greg got a new car for his birthday. He was turning 17. My parents didn't want me to get a ride with Greg, but our families had been friends for years. So they let me go. They wished later they hadn't.

We were coming home from a basketball game. I remember, it was a Wednesday. We had lost. It was **pitiful**. Greg was really mad so he was driving kind of fast. He was talking a lot too. I still remember what he was saying: "I can't believe it! The team didn't pull together. What . . ." He never got to finish his sentence. This pickup truck came around the corner all of sudden. It crossed over into our **lane** and hit us full on. I saw the headlights and then I **blacked out**.

My first memory afterwards was of my parents **leaning** over me in the hospital room. It was so sunny in the room it hurt my eyes. My Mom looked awful. She thought I'd never come back. My Dad told me Greg was dead. I started to cry. Then I asked what was wrong with me. He told me my left leg was so **mangled** that they had had to amputate it. My right leg had a rod in it now, to hold it together. I felt awful. Why did Greg have to die? I thought I'd never be able to play basketball again or even go back to school. I was afraid I wouldn't even be able to walk. I got really depressed, but my parents told me not to give up.

I left the hospital to go to a special rehabilitation centre for teens. A whole team of specialists was assigned to work with me to help me cope with my new prosthetic leg. At first I hated it. I only started to stop feeling sorry for myself when I made a new friend. Her name was Akira. She was 18. She had lost both legs in a road biking accident. She was so positive, it seemed weird to me. She told me, "I'm not going to let this get to me! I love biking and I plan on continuing." I thought Akira was nuts. "What do you mean?" I asked.

She told me about a camp she was going to in July. It was a sports camp. They even had basketball. I was doubtful at first but when she invited me, I said, "Sure!"

I went. I am so glad I did. That summer I got over my **hang-ups** and made new friends who were also overcoming physical challenges. They helped me learn to laugh at my difficulties and find a way to pursue my passion, basketball, despite my new situation.

It's been three years now since my accident. This summer Akira invited me to speak at the "Hoops of Hope" camp. She's the Camp Director now. I always end my speeches the same way: "Don't think about what you don't have. Focus on what you *do* have, and *can* do. One hoop at a time."

Explore the Text

Before Reading

1. Look at the title and the photo on page 20. Scan the text and complete the chart below.

Title	
Text Type	
Purpose	
Audience	

2. Use your resources to find the meaning of the following words that will help you understand the text.

a) pitiful _____

b) lane _____

c) blacked out _____

d) leaning _____

e) mangled _____

f) hang-ups _____

While Reading

3. Read the text. Underline sentences that describe how David coped with his accident using the four F's: family, friends, fun and focus.

After Reading

4. How is the title, "One Hoop at a Time," appropriate?

_____

_____

5. Skim the story again and put the events in order.

a) David got really depressed.	
b) Akira invited David to speak at the "Hoops of Hope" camp to share his story.	
c) David learned to cope with his new condition and learned to play basketball again.	
d) The boys were driving home from a basketball game when Greg's car was hit by a pickup truck.	
e) David's friend Greg got a new car for his birthday and David's parents let him go to the game with him.	
f) At the rehabilitation centre, David made a new friend, Akira, who helped him change his attitude about his prosthetic leg.	
g) David woke up in the hospital and his parents told him that he had had one leg amputated and the other had a rod placed in it.	

6. When David first met Akira, he thought she was really weird. Why do you think he accepted her invitation to the sports camp?

_____

_____

_____

7. David wrote that he learned to "laugh at" his difficulties and that helped him get out of his depression. Do you think he meant that we should ignore the bad things that happen to us and pretend that they aren't difficult? Explain.

_____

_____

_____

_____

_____

_____

Connect With the Text

8. Do you know of anyone who has overcome a serious challenge? How did this person cope and change as a result of his or her challenge? Write a short text describing this process.

_____

_____

_____

_____

_____

_____

Generalize

9. Think of a challenging situation that could arise in a student's life, then suggest three ways your school and fellow students could support him or her.

_____

_____

_____

_____

_____

_____

Vocabulary

Practise

A. Read the clues. Complete the crossword puzzle below. Use your dictionary.

Across:
- **2.** performances
- **6.** scraped
- **7.** travel
- **8.** badly marked
- **9.** suffered

Down:
- **1.** prepare for planting
- **3.** double meaning
- **4.** boasted
- **5.** facial characteristics
- **10.** celebration

B. Match the words with their antonyms.

1. fainted _____ **a)** telling the truth

2. ashamed _____ **b)** helps up

3. lying _____ **c)** regained consciousness

4. knocks down _____ **d)** depressed

5. undeterred _____ **e)** proud

C. Write a sentence using at least two words from part B.

_____

_____

Learn More

Use synonyms from the word bank to replace the words in parentheses in the text. Use your dictionary.

Word Bank		
• addiction	• hardship	• psychologist
• conquer	• helpline	• self-esteem
• cope	• ordeal	• skill
• disease	• overcome	• social worker
• faith	• peer pressure	• support network
• friendship		

One sure way to _____ (*beat*) and _____ (*rise above*) any

kind of _____ (*difficulty*) and _____ (*problems*)

associated with school, work, extra-curricular activities and home is to use a

_____ (*hotline for help*). There are a number to choose from.

This type of _____ (*system for assistance*) helps teens

_____ (*deal*) with _____ (*influence of other*

teens), _____ (*relational*) problems, _____

(*sickness*) and _____ (*substance abuse*). Volunteers are trained

by _____ (*experts in psychology*) and _____

(*experts in adaptation challenges*) to develop the _____ (*abilities*)

necessary to help teenagers specifically. Often by just talking, callers develop

better _____ (*how a person feels about him- or herself*), and

more _____ (*optimism*) that things will improve. Help may be

just a chat away!

Your Turn

Write a journal entry or a poem about how you reached out for help in a difficult situation. Use at least four of the vocabulary words from the word bank above.

_____

_____

_____

_____

_____

Grammar

The Present Perfect and the Past Perfect

Each of the **perfect tenses** has a different use:

You use the present perfect to express	You use the past perfect to express
• a recently completed action • an action completed at an unspecified time in the past	• a situation, habit or action that happened in the past <u>before</u> some other past event
Adverbs of time and frequency used with the present perfect: *already, always, before, for, lately, never, often, once, recently, since, yet*	Adverbs of time and frequency used with the past perfect: *already, always, as soon as, before, for, never, the moment, until, when*

Formation

Affirmative: Use the auxiliary verb *to have* and the past participle of the main verb.

The **present perfect** uses *to have* in the present: *have/has*
*Jade **has worked** as a police officer for three months.*

The **past perfect** uses *to have* in the past: *had*
*Viktor **had worked** as a nurse before he left for Europe.*

Negative: Add *not* after the auxiliary verb.
*The editor **has not/hasn't changed** the ad picture yet.*
*She **had not/hadn't noticed** how sexist the picture was before she accepted it.*

Interrogative: Start with the auxiliary verb, followed by the subject and the past participle of the main verb.

Have you ever realized how stereotypical that slogan is?
Had you noticed how stereotypical the slogan was before I mentioned it?

Reminder: The past participle of regular verbs ends in *ed* (*worked*). For irregular verbs, the past participles vary and must be learned. See Common Irregular Verbs on page 144.

→ LEARN MORE

You often use *for* and *since* with a present perfect or past perfect tense.

- *Since* is used with the present perfect when we know when the action began in the past but it's not finished yet.
  *We have had male cheerleaders at our school **since 2003**.*

- *For* is used to express the duration of an action that began in the past.
  *Raymond's grandmother has been an activist **for 40 years**. She had studied philosophy **for three years** before she went into politics.*

Frequent Errors

Read the sentences. Circle the errors. Rewrite the sentences correctly.

1. Monique have never liked wearing dresses or makeup.

   _____

2. Siobahn and Aren worked at the Censorship Board since three years.

   _____

3. Recently, a school had open up in Toronto for students who have been victims of homophobia.

   _____

   _____

4. All year, my little brother has been bully by his classmates for liking dolls.

   _____

   _____

5. Stereotyping in advertising have become a more popular topic of study in high schools.

   _____

   _____

6. Siam has feel different from other girls since she was very young?

   _____

Practise 1

Write the correct form of the present perfect or past perfect in the following sentences.

1. Tremayne _____ (*to hand in*, negative) his report on male stereotyping in advertising.

2. How long _____ Liam and Akanke _____ (*to work*) at social services?

3. Before the Second World War broke out, women _____ (*to have*, negative) much experience working out of the home.

4. It's clear that the people _____ really _____ (*to understand*, negative) how bigotry affects them.

5. Until my father decided to stay home to take care of me and my sister, my mother
   _____ (*to have*) a hard time trying to earn money and take care of
   the family.

6. Will Christophe _____ (*to finish*) his hairdressing course by April?

7. Miranda and Enrique _____ already _____ (*to prepare*) for a
   year when they went to South Africa to open the women's shelter.

8. In the film *Boys Don't Cry,* Brandon Teena _____ (*to be*) the popular
   new guy in town before his friends discovered Brandon was transgendered.

9. I don't believe the types of toys designed for boys and girls _____ really
   _____ (*to change*) much since I was a child.

10. Even though he is a guy, my cousin Franz _____ always _____
    (*to say*) that he is a feminist.

Practise 2

Complete the sentences with the correct form of the verb in the perfect tense.

Video game designers _____
(*to change*) video games on three fronts:
content, characters and colour. This
started to happen after researchers
_____ (*to observe*)
that while many boys enjoy action and
violence, the majority of girls enjoy problem-solving and role-playing. Game content
is starting to reflect these interests. As well, gender representation in game characters
_____ (*to start*) to become more balanced after a study showed that
over 90% of games contained male characters, while only around 50% featured female
characters. Furthermore, before video games began to change, many game players
_____ (*to observe*) that most female characters were hyper-sexualized,
stereotypical, unrealistic or were the victims of violence. Finally, first impressions count,
so you may _____ (*to notice*) that the colours of consoles sold now
_____ (*to change*) from only black or grey, to pink and purple as well.

Your Turn

Write a short text expressing your opinion on the previous text. Do you believe that video game content has changed much recently? Are video game characters stereotypical? Does console colour make a difference? Use the perfect tenses as much as possible.

_____

_____

_____

_____

_____

_____

_____

_____

_____

The Comparative and Superlative of Adjectives

You can use the **comparative** and **superlative** forms of adjectives to indicate superiority, inferiority, or equality.

Formation	Comparative	Superlative
Adjectives of one syllable: *short, young*	Add **er:** *shorter, younger*	Add **est:** *shortest, youngest*
Adjectives of one syllable that end in one vowel and a consonant: *big, hot*	Double the final consonant and add **er:** *bigger, hotter*	Double the final consonant and add **est:** *biggest, hottest*
Adjectives of two syllables ending in *y: pretty, crazy*	Change *y* to **ier:** *prettier, crazier*	Change *y* to **iest:** *prettiest, craziest*
Adjectives of two or more syllables: *active, energetic*	Add **more/less** before the adjective: *more active, less energetic*	Add **most/least** before the adjective: *most active, least energetic*
Irregular adjectives: *bad, good, many, little, old*	*worse, better, more, less, older*	*worst, best, most, least, oldest*

- For comparisons of **superiority**, use the comparative with *than*.

  Keith thinks women are braver than men.

  Are men more exploited than women in advertising?

- For comparisons of **inferiority**, use *less* or *less . . . than* with the basic form of the adjective.

  I believe female athletes are less arrogant than male athletes.

> • For comparisons of **equality**, use the basic form of the adjective with *as . . . as*.
> *Boys are as capable as girls when it comes to babysitting.*
>
> • To say something is **the greatest** or **the least**, use the superlative form of the adjective with *the*.
> *In this book, the female vampire is the toughest character, while the male vampire is the least dangerous.*

Frequent Errors

Underline the error in each sentence. Write the correct form on the line.

1. My uncle Raphael is the baddest driver. _____

2. The female producer got the job because she was the goodest candidate.

_____

3. Who do you think are funnyer: male or female comedians? _____

4. Suri is more faster and competiver that Max. _____

5. Jean-Claude is the more talented at sewing in the class. _____

Practise 1

Read the text, then underline the comparatives and circle the superlatives.

Who makes the most effective principal: a woman or a man? The question is more difficult to answer than you might think. Although some people claim that men are usually more authoritative and more consistent in their emotions, others find women more sensitive to the needs of the students and the demands of the parents. Women are also more skilled at multitasking since they often manage home and a career. Some may argue men are better able to make tough decisions, because they believe women to be more emotional. Is this really true? And are men the more ambitious of the two? Impossible to tell. The bottom line is that men are as multitalented as women. One is not better than the other. In fact, it is impossible to say which is the more likely to benefit a school. Hey, maybe you've got what it takes to be the best principal!

Practise 2

Complete the sentences with the correct forms of the adjectives in the following text.

Over the past five years, single-sex public education has become _____ (*popular*). Many policy makers and curriculum designers think that co-ed schools are _____ (*likely*) to reinforce gender stereotypes than single-gender settings. However, single-sex schools are not necessarily the _____ (*efficient*) way to neutralize gender stereotyping as sometimes they can be _____ (*traditional*) than other academic institutions. Girls are raised to be "ladies" and boys are trained to become "leaders." Nonetheless, single-sex schools usually offer girls a _____ (*wide*) variety of math, science and computer-related classes. Boys, on the other hand, are offered a _____ (*great*) opportunity to enjoy artistic classes (e.g. art, drama, foreign languages and music). Many experts agree, however, that _____ (*good*) way to beat gender stereotypes is to be _____ (*attentive*) to individual students' needs.

Practise 3

For each of the set of clues, write: 1) one comparison of equality, 2) one comparative and 3) one superlative when possible, i.e. when you are comparing three or more things.

1. A female anchor . . . a male anchor . . . credible

   _____

   _____

2. Teenage boys . . . teenage girls . . . college boys . . . college girls . . . interested in gossip

   _____

   _____

   _____

3. Women's voices . . . men's voices . . . soothing – negative

   _____

   _____

   _____

4. My father . . . mother . . . strict – negative

_____

_____

5. Men . . . women . . . good at saving money

_____

_____

Your Turn

Many schools admit only boys or only girls. What do you think are the advantages and disadvantages of having single-sex schools? Write a short text to justify your opinion, comparing both situations. Use the comparative and superlative in making your point.

_____

_____

_____

_____

_____

_____

_____

Read and Respond

Vive la Différence!
Is It All in the Brain?

In this article, the author explores what makes men and women tick differently!

By Shakila Pierdomenico

"What the heck was he thinking?"
"Why on earth is she asking me that—again?"

You may have already asked this kind of question. So, what makes men and women tick? Are our brains really so different? This is a complex question, one that requires looking at biology and neurology for answers.

→

Analyses of the brains of women and men show a number of physiological differences.

Brain size: At birth, boys usually have 12–30% larger brains than girls. However, this is proportional to birth weight. So if a baby boy and girl weigh the same, their brains will be the same size too. However, males have 4% more brain cells than women.

Corpus callosum: The corpus callosum serves as a link between the two sides of the brain. Data transfer occurs here. Some scientists believe women have a larger and more developed corpus callosum which facilitates data transfer. If this is true, it means women can transfer information from one side of the brain to the other faster than men.

Limbic system: This part of your brain basically takes care of emotions and memories. Women have a larger limbic system. This enables women to be more in touch with their feelings, and express them better than men.

Hypothalamus: The hypothalamus is one part of the limbic system and it works as the "thermostat" of the body, regulating functions like hunger, thirst, sleep-wake cycles, temperature, mating behaviours and reproductive cycles. The only differences noted here are that the part of the hypothalamus taking care of mating behaviour is greater in volume in males, while the part that regulates reproduction cycles is shaped differently in women and men.

It has been argued that there are three brain types: the "female" brain, the "male" brain and the "balanced" one. The female brain tends to prioritize empathizing over systematizing, while the male brain does the opposite. The balanced brain strikes a balance between the two . . . but none of these brains is "better" than the others. Which one do you think you have?

Keep in mind, however: being a guy doesn't mean you have a male brain, necessarily, or being a girl, that you have a female brain. This explains why guys can be dedicated nurses and girls can be fearless firefighters.

So, while you may be a guy with a few more brain cells than a girl, or a girl with a greater capacity to handle information, don't be surprised if you're a guy who makes a great listener or a girl who shines in the physics lab! It's all in the programming of your brain.

VOCABULARY

in touch with: aware of

mating behaviour: actions leading to reproduction

empathizing: understanding another's feelings

systematizing: arranging according to a system

shines: excels

Explore the Text

Before Reading

1. Read the title of the article. How do you think the author will explain differences in male and female behaviour?

_____

_____

2. Do you believe that boys' and girls' brains are different? In what ways?

_____

_____

3. List some of the functions of the brain that you know.

_____

_____

While Reading

4. As you read the article, write down the details you learn about brain differences in men and women.

Difference in . . .	Details
a) Brain size	
b) Corpus callosum	
c) Limbic system	
d) Hypothalamus	
e) Brain gender	

After Reading

5. Match the following brain activities to the part of your brain responsible.

   a) The right side of your brain is communicating with the left side.

   _____

   b) You're remembering your last birthday. _____

   c) You're yawning and wanting a snack. _____

   d) Walking into the exam room fills you with terror. _____

   e) You send a text to someone you find cute. _____

Connect With the Text

6. What type of brain do you think you have? Support your answer with examples from your everyday life.

   _____

   _____

   _____

   _____

7. Do you think it is possible to develop a balanced brain? Explain.

   _____

   _____

   _____

   _____

   _____

   _____

   _____

Generalize

8. How do you think society would be different if everyone were androgynous and had balanced brains? Explain.

   _____

   _____

   _____

   _____

Vocabulary

Practise

Use the words from the word bank to complete the sentences.

Word Bank		
• bigotry	• indifferent	• prejudices
• bumbling	• intuitive	• put down
• chiselled	• nurturing	• unassuming
• gasp	• pitiful	• veiled

1. Woman are often portrayed as being _____ and _____ .

2. The male heroes in comic books often have strong, _____ features.

3. The Special Ed. teacher explained that _____ means intolerance of differences.

4. The public's indifferent response to the slander was _____ .

5. We all let out a _____ when we learned that women still earn about 25% less than men.

6. Though she is famous, the president of the record company is a very _____ person.

7. Some films _____ sensitive guys, by making them look like nerds.

8. Audiences often laugh at _____ male characters as they try to get out of a mess, not realizing the implications of this kind of comedy cliché.

9. Subliminal messages are _____ so efficiently that people often don't realize what they are seeing.

10. Female firefighters have to work hard to combat people's _____ , such as "women are the weaker sex."

Learn More

Match the definitions with the vocabulary words.

1. observant _____
2. not aware _____
3. great pride in being male _____
4. working together or communicating _____
5. not knowing _____
6. femaleness _____
7. reflection _____
8. sympathy _____
9. maleness _____
10. sending and receiving of messages _____

a) compassion
b) consideration
c) femininity
d) perceptive
e) masculinity
f) interaction
g) oblivious
h) ignorant
i) communication
j) machismo

Your Turn

Choose one topic below. Use the vocabulary from the previous exercise in a short text to express your opinion.

a) How have the roles of men and women in movies changed over the past generation?

b) How do the characters of the heroes and heroines in popular children's stories compare?

c) How do you imagine the ideal man and woman in the future?

_____

_____

_____

_____

_____

_____

_____

_____

_____

_____

_____

Grammar

The Future

You can use **the future** to describe

- an intended action — *We **will look** for an apartment next week.*

- a future state — *She **will be** very busy.*

- predictable future events — *Lucy **will write** the final exams at the end of the year.*

- probable future results — *If we read the classified ads every day, we **will find** an apartment quite soon.*

Formation

Affirmative*	Negative*	Interrogative
I, You, He/She/It, We, They will get a job this summer.	*I, You, He/She/It, We, They will not get a job this summer.*	*Will I, you, he/she/it, we, they get a job this summer?*

* In everyday English, use the contracted form of *will* (*'ll*) and *will not* (*won't*).

Affirmative: Use the auxiliary *will* with the base form of the main verb in all cases.

Negative: Add *not* after the auxiliary to make a negative statement.

Interrogative: To ask a question, start with the auxiliary *will*, followed by the subject and the base form of the main verb.

Time markers: *in a week/month, next Monday/week/month/year, soon, this summer/winter, tomorrow,* etc.

Reminder: The verb *to be* follows the same rules as other verbs in the simple future. *I **will be** at the job workshop. **Will** you **be** there? Grace **won't be**.*

→ LEARN MORE

- The auxiliary verb *shall* is sometimes used instead of *will* in formal English, especially in the interrogative. *Where **shall** we **meet** tonight?*

- Another way of expressing or asking about future intentions is to use the simple present of the auxiliary verb *to be* + *going to* and the base form of the main verb.
  *We **are going to study** very hard to ace the exams.*
  *I'm **not going to waste** any more time.*
  ***Are** you **going to apply** to CEGEP?*

- You can use the **present continuous** to talk about definite plans in the near future.
  *We **are meeting** friends at the airport on Saturday.*
  *Is Liam **coming** to the concert in June?*

- You can use the **simple future** tense to express opinions, assumptions or guesses about the future.
  Use verbs like *to believe, to think, to suppose, to doubt, to expect, to hope* and *to know* in the present tense to introduce your idea. Use the simple future for your prediction.
  *I **believe** that we will all pass English.*
  *I **doubt** that Tristan will fail anything.*

The Future Continuous

You can use the **future continuous** to describe

- an action that will be happening at a specific point in the future   *Joanne **will be leaving** for New York tomorrow.*

- an ongoing action in the future   *Molly **will be having** interviews all week.*

Formation

Affirmative*	Negative*	Interrogative
I, You, He/She/It, We, They **will be** *moving.*	*I, You, He/She/It, We, They* **will not be** *moving.*	*Will I, you, he/she/it, we, they be moving?*

* In everyday English, use the contracted form of *will* (*'ll*) and *will not* (*won't*).

Affirmative: Use *will be* (the future tense of the auxiliary verb *to be*) and the present participle of the main verb.

Negative: Use *will not be* with the present participle of the main verb to make a negative statement.

Interrogative: To ask a question, start with the auxiliary *will*, followed by the subject, *be*, and the present participle of the main verb.

Time markers: *in (three) days/weeks/months, soon, by then/tomorrow/Monday, later, all afternoon/day/month,* etc.

Frequent Errors

Circle the simple future and future continuous errors. Rewrite the sentences correctly.

1. I am finish high school this year and it be a big deal for me.

_____

_____

2. I will moving away to go to CEGEP, which means that I get an apartment with my best friend.

_____

_____

3. We have been friends since first grade, so I don't think that we have problems living together.

_____

_____

4. Next year, we living together.

_____

5. This weekend, we are go apartment hunting in the city.

_____

6. Your mom is a real estate agent. She will give us some advice?

_____

Practise

Complete the text with the simple future tense of the verbs in parentheses.

As my best friend and I get ready to move in together, there are a few things we _____ (*to need*) to do.

First of all, we _____ (*to have*) to find the perfect apartment. Now this _____ (*to be*, negative) just any apartment. It needs to be cool, roomy and in the right neighbourhood. We _____ (*to make + also*) certain that we each have a big bedroom. Since we _____ (*to be*) full-time students we _____ (*to want*) to be able to study in our rooms without being disturbed. Next, we have decided that we _____ (*to make*) a schedule of who _____ (*to cook*). We agree that we _____ (*to starve*, negative) just because we're living on our own, and we _____ (*to eat*, negative) macaroni and cheese every day, either!

Your Turn

Complete the sentences with the future continuous to describe what you'll be doing at different times in your life.

1. In one hour, _____

2. Tomorrow at this time, _____

3. Next weekend, _____

4. When I graduate, _____

5. When I turn 21, _____

Conditional Sentences

Conditional sentences have two parts: the if-clause, which describes the condition, and the main clause, which describes the potential result.

You can use conditional sentences to describe

- a probable event   *If she earns enough money* (condition), *she will be able to travel.*
- a possible event   *He could rent a car if he gets a licence* (condition).
- an unreal event   *We would climb Mount Everest if we could* (condition).

For Probable or Possible Events

- **If-clause:** Use the simple present.

- **Main clause:** Use the future to indicate an intention or a probable result.
  *If I **pass** my exams, I **will go** to CEGEP.*
  *Your Spanish **will improve** if you **take** extra lessons.*

- You can indicate that events in the main clause are more or less probable by using the modal auxiliaries *may, can* or *should* with the base form of the verb.
  *If I **pass** my exams, I **may go** to CEGEP.* (possibility)
  *Your Spanish **should improve** if you **take** extra lessons.* (strong probability)

For Unreal Events

To refer to present or future conditions that could still be fulfilled but are improbable:

- **If-clause:** Use the simple past.

- **Main clause:** Use the present conditional.
  *If we **had** a bigger apartment, we **would entertain** more.*
  *Your Spanish **would improve** if you **took** extra lessons.*

Reminder: For the verb *to be*, use *were* in the if-clause.

*If I, you, he/she/it, we, you, they **were** bigger, . . .*

Frequent Errors

Circle the error in each sentence and indicate whether it is in the main clause (M) or the if-clause (I). Then write down the correct verb.

1. If I take a gap year, I am behind in my studies. _____

2. I would take a trip if I would have enough money. _____

3. If I was you, I wouldn't take a gap year. _____

4. You get lost if you don't take a map. _____

5. You would be late if you do not leave now. _____

Practise 1

Complete the sentences with the appropriate form of the verbs in parentheses. At the end of each sentence, write *P* to indicate a probable or possible conditional and *U* to indicate an unreal conditional.

1. If I _____ (*to have*) enough money, I will take a gap year. _____

2. If I _____ (*to have*) enough money, I would take a gap year. _____

3. If I _____ (*to take*) a gap year, I would go on an expedition to the Arctic. _____

4. If I _____ (*to take*) a gap year, I will go on an expedition to the Arctic. _____

5. I would take a gap year if I _____ (*to be*) you. _____

6. If he _____ (*to be*) braver, he wouldn't be afraid to come on the Arctic expedition. _____

7. If he _____ (*to tell*) you about it, try to encourage him to go. _____

8. Tell him that if he _____ (*to go*), he might see some polar bears. _____

Practise 2

A. Combine each pair of phrases to make a probable or a possible conditional sentence. Use contractions where appropriate.

1. plan your gap year in advance – have a better experience

   _____

   _____

2. save money – work with a travel company

   _____

   _____

3. plan your trip on your own – get exactly what you want

_____

_____

4. feel more secure – travel with a friend

_____

_____

5. know the person well – have fewer surprises

_____

_____

B. Combine each pair of phrases to make an unreal conditional sentence.

1. love winter camping – try it

_____

2. know where you are going – buy a map

_____

3. be happy (negative) – get lost

_____

4. enjoy it (negative) – have to spend a night in the woods

_____

5. spend a night in the woods with the bears – sleep very well (negative)

_____

_____

Your Turn

Write about an adventure that you would like to have during a gap year. Include at least two probable and two improbable conditional sentences, and underline them.

_____

_____

_____

_____

_____

_____

_____

Read and Respond

Top Five First Apartment Mistakes

The time when you will be living on
your own is getting closer and closer.
Becoming better informed before you
start apartment hunting can save you a
5 lot of headaches later. These top five
apartment mistakes will get you started.

Mistake #1: Paying Too Much

This is the most common beginner's
mistake. It is easy to forget that rent is
10 only one of the expenses you will have to
deal with when you are living on your
own. You will also have to pay for electricity, Internet, cable and phone, not to
mention food, personal expenses and commuting to work or school. You may even
want to have some money left over for hanging out with your friends at the corner
15 café. If you spend more than a third of your salary on rent, you will regret it.

Mistake #2: Bad Location, Bad Location, Bad Location

No matter how good the apartment is, a bad location can ruin it. Your friends may
come over once to see your great living room with the amazing view, but if they
have to travel an hour to get there, you will never get them to visit again. A long
20 commute to work or school will soon get to you, too. Finally, your up-and-coming
area, touted by the real estate agent, may be terrifying after dark.

Mistake #3: Picking the Wrong Roommate

You are a neat freak and your roommate is a slob. You need to get to work at 6 a.m.
and your roommate parties late at night. Opposites may attract but will not make
25 the best roommates. Know what you are getting into and make sure that you have
an agreement with a future roommate before you move in, even if you know each
other well.

Mistake #4: Not Reading the Lease

You are responsible for the apartment until the end of
30 your lease and you will have to find someone to sublet
if you decide to move out early. Study the wording
of the lease carefully and if you do not understand
something, find out what it means before signing on
the dotted line. The Québec provincial rental board
35 is a great place to look for information about possible
problems. There are no excuses for not knowing what
you are getting into!

> **VOCABULARY**
>
> **commuting:** travelling
> **get to:** annoy
> **lease:** contract
> **neat freak:** very tidy person
> **slob:** untidy person
> **splurging:** spending a lot of money
> **sublet:** rent from original tenant
> **up-and-coming:** becoming more desirable

Mistake #5: Spending Too Much on Furnishings

40 **Splurging** on a 42-inch flat screen TV might mean that you will be spending all your free time in front of it because you cannot afford to go out. Before you charge your dream sofa and bed to your credit card, remember that you will still be paying for
45 them long after you have moved to your next apartment, if you are not careful.

Source: MyFirstApartment.com

Explore the Text

Before Reading

1. When do you think you will be living on your own? What kind of future home do you imagine you will have?

_____

_____

_____

2. What challenges do you think you might face when you move into your first apartment?

_____

_____

_____

While Reading

3. Find all the simple future and future continuous verbs in the text on pages 44–45. Write them down below, with the line number from the article.

Simple future	Future continuous
_____	_____
_____	_____
_____	_____
_____	_____
_____	_____
_____	_____

After Reading

4. Reword each mistake as a tip. Then write down what you could do to avoid making the mistake.

Tip	How to Avoid Making the Mistake
_____ _____ _____	_____ _____ _____
_____ _____ _____	_____ _____ _____
_____ _____ _____	_____ _____ _____
_____ _____ _____	_____ _____ _____
_____ _____ _____	_____ _____ _____

5. What is the maximum portion of your income that you should spend on rent?

_____

6. What are three possible consequences of choosing a poor location?

_____

_____

_____

7. What are two possible consequences of not choosing a roommate carefully?

_____

_____

8. What is one solution if you have to break your lease?

_____

Connect With the Text

9. Which of the five mistakes are you most likely to make? Put them in order from the one you are most likely to make to the one you are least likely to make. Then write the reason why you might or might not make each mistake.

Mistake	Reason
1.	
2.	
3.	
4.	
5.	

Generalize

10. What other problems might people encounter in their first apartment? How could each problem be avoided? Write about three possible problems.

_____

_____

_____

_____

11. What do you hope your first experience of living in your own apartment will be like? Write a paragraph about it. Look at the answers you gave in Step 10 for ideas. Include reasons for your ideas and use the future tenses.

_____

_____

_____

_____

_____

_____

_____

_____

_____

_____

Vocabulary

Practise

Word Bank		
• a lot on my plate	• discount	• slipping
• back on track	• learn the ropes	• sort of
• common-law	• raided	

A. Write down a synonym from the word bank for each of the following groups. Use your dictionary if necessary.

1.
unmarried couple,
sharing a home

_____

2.
getting organized,
in control

_____

3.
sale, special,
great deal

_____

4.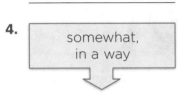
somewhat,
in a way

_____

5.
take from,
rob, invade

_____

6.
deteriorating,
getting worse

_____

B. Cross out the word or expression in each sentence that does not fit and replace it with the correct word or expression from the word bank.

1. With all my assignments, my job and my dog, I feel like I have a break.

_____

2. I knew if I wanted to quit at my new job, I would have to work very hard.

_____

3. I was able to get a great increase on the price because this is last year's model.

_____

4. The married couple decided to get married. _____

5. I didn't realize my savings were improving so badly. I'll have to make a budget.

_____

6. Once I get these bills paid, I'll feel like I'm disorganized. _____

7. Jon's apartment was entirely clean, but he still had dirty dishes in the sink.

_____

8. When I got home, I discovered that my roommate had filled the fridge. There was

nothing left to eat! _____

Learn More

Word Bank		
• advice	• dependability	• occupation
• career	• dilemma	• quest
• conscientious	• guidance	

Complete the text with words from the word bank.

Welcome to the Employment Emporium! This website contains useful _____ for everyone out there who's looking for a new _____ . Finding another _____ can present a _____ for even the most experienced job hunter. There are a few qualities that all prospective employers look for, such as _____ . Employers also want someone who is _____ . As you embark on your _____ , remember this: Job-hunting is not for the faint of heart! With our _____ you will soon find a job that you love.

Your Turn

Use at least five of the words in a short text to describe what you would look for in an employee.

_____

_____

_____

_____

_____

_____

_____

_____

_____

_____

_____

Humans, Animals and Ethics

Grammar

Transition Words

You use transition words to connect two sentences or clauses which have similar or different ideas. They add clarity and flow to writing and speech. They also indicate whether the idea that follows is more important, less important, of equal importance or in contrast to what has already been written. Note that most transitions are used at the beginning of a sentence or a clause.

- **To add another idea:** *and, also, besides, furthermore, in addition, moreover, as well as*
  My family loves to eat meat. **Furthermore**, *we believe it's good to support farmers.*

- **To compare two different ideas:** *but, however, instead, on the other hand, nevertheless, yet*
  Zoos are unethical, **yet** *so many people still enjoy them.*

- **To contrast ideas:** *although, despite the fact that, even if, even though*
  Although *my brother is a vegan, he occasionally eats ice cream.*

- **To indicate a reason:** *because, since, as, for*
  He didn't buy that jacket **because** *it has fur on the hood.*

- **To advance a narrative:** *after, after that, as soon as, at first, before, during, finally, for a while, immediately, in the late afternoon, later, later on, meanwhile, next, suddenly, then, when, while*
  At first *we wanted a big dog.* **Then** *we realized big dogs need a lot of walking.*

- **To state a consequence:** *therefore, consequently, as a result, hence, thus, for this reason, because of this, so*
  Animals are often abused in circuses. **For this reason**, *I only go to circuses that don't use animal performers.*

- **To reinforce an idea:** *as a matter of fact, in fact, indeed, of course*
  Animals, **of course**, *are necessary to humans.*

- **To express a condition:** *if, as long as, provided that, assuming that*
  Anyone can become a vegetarian, **provided that** *you commit to it.*

- **To structure or sequence ideas:** *first, firstly, first of all; second, secondly, third, etc., next, finally, in conclusion, to conclude, lastly*
  Finally, *why not volunteer at your local animal shelter?*

Frequent Errors

Underline the transition word error in each sentence, then write the correct transition word on the line below. There may be more than one correct answer.

1. In conclusion, I will begin by telling you my opinion about domestic animals.

   _____

2. I love animals but I have a pet.

   _____

3. I work in a pet store. On the other hand, I think pet stores are great.

   _____

4. Some people don't trust pet stores, additionally they adopt animals from the SPCA.

   _____

5. Others buy dogs from puppy mills nevertheless the dogs aren't treated well.

   _____

Practise 1

Underline the transition words which join the clauses to make a logical sentence.

1. Jeffrey Masson has written a book about the emotional lives of animals (*because/ despite the fact that*) he finds the subject fascinating.

2. He is a writer (*in addition to/consequently*) being a university professor.

3. Masson kept writing about animals after he wrote *When Elephants Weep*; (*finally/in fact*), he has written 10 books on this subject!

4. Masson has continued promoting his ideas (*despite the fact that/for this reason*) the scientific community does not support him.

5. Masson has always loved animals; (*as a matter of fact/however*), what he learned about animals when he was younger turned him into an animal activist.

6. Writing *The Pig Who Sang to the Moon* taught Masson a lot about the emotional lives of farm animals; (*to conclude/as a result*) he became a vegan.

Practise 2

Read the paragraph and use a transition from the word bank to fill in each blank.

Word Bank		
• as long as	• finally	• in fact
• despite	• hence	• meanwhile

Most pet owners will readily agree that their own cats, dogs, birds and horses feel

emotions. _____ , scientists continue to dispute that animals can feel,

_____ so much anecdotal evidence. _____ , it is true

that various animals react in different ways and we can't be sure what those reactions

might mean, _____ the debates on this subject. _____

there is a chance that animals have feelings, shouldn't we treat them with more care?

And _____ , can we really justify using them in the ways we do?

Your Turn

Complete the sentences using logical endings based on the transition words provided.

1. Although I have never read about animals having emotions before, _____

_____

2. Animals may experience emotions; however, _____

_____

3. Despite what scientists think about animals having emotions, _____

_____

4. I am not sure if animals really experience joy, love or sadness, yet _____

_____

5. Some people think it's cruel to use wool or silk. Furthermore, _____

_____

6. My cousin and I stopped eating chicken since _____

_____

7. Researchers will continue to use animals for testing as long as _____

_____

8. We should pay more attention to how animals are feeling because _____

_____

9. We would all benefit if people ate less meat. In fact, _____

_____

10. Not everyone agrees with Masson; nevertheless, _____

_____

Pronouns

You use **pronouns** to replace nouns in a sentence. They can help you avoid repetition. Use pronouns only when necessary. A sentence can become confusing and meaningless if too many pronouns are used.

- **Personal Pronouns:** You can use personal pronouns as subject pronouns and object pronouns.
  - A **subject pronoun** replaces a subject noun.

    Kerry is walking the dog. She walks the dog for an hour.

  - An **object pronoun** replaces a noun that is the direct or indirect object of a verb or object of the preposition.

    I gave Baz a canary. I gave him a cage, too.

- **Reflexive Pronouns:** You use reflexive pronouns as the direct or indirect object of a verb when the subject and object are the same.

  I told myself not to forget to feed our pet cobra. It can't feed itself in a cage.

- **Relative Pronouns:** You use relative pronouns to replace a noun or pronoun as the subject or object of a relative clause.

  Reminder: They are often confused with interrogative pronouns.

  The shampoo that I bought was not tested on animals. The person who sold me the shampoo was very knowledgeable.

- **Interrogative Pronouns:** You use interrogative pronouns at the beginning of a sentence to ask for information about people, events or things.

  Who is vegetarian? What should we do? Which do you think is correct?

- **Possessive Pronouns:** You use possessive pronouns to replace a noun and a possessive adjective. It draws attention to the possessor and will help you avoid repeating the noun.

  Is that Will's guide dog? Yes, it's his.

- **Demonstrative Pronouns:** You use demonstrative pronouns to replace a noun and a demonstrative adjective. It draws attention to the noun without repeating it. Use *this* and *that* for singular nouns, and *these* and *those* for plural nouns.

  This is my new kitten. Those are all its toys. Yes, you told me that.

Personal Pronouns		Reflexive Pronouns	Possessive Pronouns
Subject	**Object**		
I	*me*	*myself*	*mine*
you	*you*	*yourself*	*yours*
she	*her*	*herself*	*hers*
he	*him*	*himself*	*his*
it	*it*	*itself*	*its*
we	*us*	*ourselves*	*ours*
you	*you*	*yourselves*	*yours*
they	*them*	*themselves*	*theirs*

Relative Pronouns

people: *who* (subject)
          whose (possessive)
objects: *that/which* (subject)
         which (object)
         whose (possessive)

Demonstrative Pronouns

this/that, these/those

Interrogative Pronouns

who, whose, what, which

Frequent Errors

Practise your editing skills. Cross out the pronoun errors in the text and write the correct pronouns above the crossed-out words.

Charles Darwin once wrote about canine consciousness. Charles Darwin said that old dogs have excellent memories and that old dogs have imagination. It said you can see it when them are dreaming, how their remembering the past pleasures of the chase. Darwin also wondered what cows feel when she surround and stare at a dying companion. The great scientist asked his many questions about the subject of animal consciousness.

Practise 1

To avoid repetition, underline the words which should be replaced with pronouns. Write the pronouns above the underlined words.

1. Darwin also studied how animals act when animals are afraid.

2. When Darwin compared animals and humans, Darwin found that animals and humans have many of the same behaviours.

3. Darwin discovered that when we need to escape, both human and animal hearts beat faster. The stress makes human and animal hearts push blood more quickly to human and animal muscles.

4. When frightened, a gorilla's legs shake and a dolphin's teeth chatter, showing the gorilla's and dolphin's fear.

5. Such familiar behaviour in animals touches humans. This familiar behaviour helps humans identify with animals.

Practise 2

Complete the sentences with the appropriate reflexive pronouns.

1. We enjoyed _____ when we played with our uncle's new guide dog.

2. The guide dog instructors all described _____ as animal lovers.

3. I found _____ thinking it might be fun to train guide dogs as a career.

4. The guide dog scratched _____ before falling asleep in the car.

5. Jimmy gave _____ time to become used to the guide dog.

Practise 3

Complete the sentences with the appropriate pronouns.

1. Jeffrey Masson met with Diana Reiss, a leading dolphin researcher, to ask _____ about her work. _____ was curious about whether Diana thought the dolphins were happy. Diana replied that the dolphins seemed to enjoy themselves because _____ ate well, were healthy and _____ seemed to like the games that Diana invented for _____ . Looking at the dolphins in the tank, Masson wondered if perhaps human standards of happiness are not the same as _____ .

2. In his book, Masson describes Alex, an African grey parrot _____ had an astonishing vocabulary. When his owner left _____ at the veterinarian's office, Alex screamed, "Come here! I love you. _____ am sorry. I want to go back." _____ had learned how to connect the concepts of love, staying together and being sorry with _____ feelings!

3. I lost my copy of *When Elephants Weep,* so my brother lent me _____ . My brother wants to study marine biology when _____ goes to university. Loving animals runs in _____ family. Our aunt works at the SPCA and _____ always gives both of _____ books and DVDs about animals for _____ birthdays.

⊦ Your Turn

Write about a time when you witnessed an animal experiencing an emotion. Use pronouns to avoid repetition. Underline the pronouns and use arrows to show which nouns they are replacing.

_____

_____

_____

_____

_____

_____

_____

_____

_____

_____

Read and Respond

'Hail' From the Chimp: Zoo Ape Stockpiles Stones to Throw at Visitors

CBC News – When Santino the chimpanzee began throwing rocks at zoo visitors in the summer of 1997, officials at the Swedish zoo had to wonder: where was he getting all of the ammo?

5 The answer, they discovered, was in a series of secret caches, where the chimpanzee had calmly collected—and in some cases manufactured—projectiles for later use.

According to Swedish researcher Mathias Osvath, it's "the first unambiguous evidence" of an animal other than humans making plans in one mental state for a future mental state, in this case, an agitated display of dominance from the lone
10 male chimpanzee at the zoo.

"These observations convincingly show that our fellow apes do consider the future in a very complex way," said Osvath of Lund University, in a statement.

"When wild chimps collect stones or go out to war, they probably plan this in advance. I would guess that they plan much of their everyday behaviour," he said.

Born in 1978, Santino became the dominant male at the zoo in 1994 and the only male a year later when the other male died. For his first three years of dominance the act of throwing stones across the **moat** separating the chimps from zoo visitors was infrequent.

However, in June 1997, zoo officials noted his stone throwing increased dramatically, with demonstrations involving the throwing of 10 or more projectiles if not **curtailed**—what one caretaker described as "hail storms."

A zoo worker placed herself in a **blind** to observe the chimpanzee's behaviour and found that, for five consecutive days before the opening of the zoo, Santino gathered stones from the water and placed them in the caches.

The following year, the chimpanzee added pieces of concrete to his ammunition, and was observed gently knocking on concrete rocks to break off smaller, disc-shaped pieces.

Since the initial finding, caretakers at the zoo have removed hundreds of caches, and the gathering of stones has been observed on at least 50 occasions, Osvath reported.

Osvath said while many apes have been observed collecting stones for nut cracking or other planning behaviour, it has been unclear whether the ape was doing the work to meet a current or future need: that is, is the ape looking to crack nuts because he is hungry now, or because he expects to be hungry?

Santino's stone-**gathering** however, is a clear case of planning for the future, Osvath said, since the calm manner in which the chimpanzee collected the stones differed from the agitated state in which he later **hurled** them.

VOCABULARY

ammo: ammunition (slang)
blind: a hidden place used for observing animals
curtailed: stopped
display: show
fellow: members of the same group
gathering: collecting
hurled: threw
moat: water barrier
stockpiles: collects and saves

Source: CBC March 13, 2009

Explore the Text

Before Reading

1. Do you think only some animal species have emotions? If so, which?

_____

_____

2. Why do you think scientists resist the notion that animals have feelings?

_____

_____

While Reading

3. Underline phrases that describe Santino the chimp's unusual behaviour.

4. Circle the pronouns used in the text. (Note: Do not circle the possessive adjectives, which are followed by nouns.)

After Reading

5. What message do you think Santino was trying to send by throwing stones?

_____

_____

_____

6. Explain the steps Santino the chimp follows to throw stones. Use pronouns and transition words.

_____

_____

_____

7. What words in the text describe the emotional state the chimp is in when he collects the projectiles? Give the line number where you found the words.

_____

_____

8. What words in the text describe the emotional state the chimp is in when he throws the projectiles? Give the line number where you found the words.

_____

_____

9. What do the caretakers at the zoo do to curtail Santino's stone throwing?

_____

_____

10. Why do the scientists find this behaviour remarkable?

_____

_____

_____

11. Complete these sentences using vocabulary words from the text.

  a) Santino the chimpanzee _____ rocks at zoo visitors.

  b) He spent his time _____ projectiles and hiding them.

  c) It's possible that he wanted to _____ his dominance to

  his _____ chimps.

  d) It turns out that he was getting stones from the _____
  which surrounds his home.

  e) The caretakers _____ his activities by taking away the
  projectiles.

  f) It would be fascinating to hide in a _____ to study chimps.

Connect With the Text

12. What aspect of Santino's behaviour do you find the most surprising?

_____

_____

_____

13. Do you believe that animals other than chimps can "think" as this text would
suggest? Explain your answer.

_____

_____

_____

_____

_____

_____

_____

_____

_____

_____

_____

_____

_____

▪ Generalize

14. Should we keep animals in zoos? Are zoos ethical? Are there good reasons to keep zoos as they are? Justify your answer. Use transition words to connect your ideas and pronouns to avoid repetition.

_____

_____

_____

_____

_____

_____

_____

_____

_____

_____

_____

Vocabulary

▪ Practise

A. Match the words with their definitions.

1. startled _____	**a)** about to happen
2. grouchy _____	**b)** not injured
3. hugs _____	**c)** surprised
4. boisterous _____	**d)** unwillingly
5. wounds _____	**e)** rough and noisy
6. unharmed _____	**f)** injuries
7. accurately _____	**g)** precisely
8. repulsed _____	**h)** in a bad mood
9. reluctantly _____	**i)** disgusted
10. impending _____	**j)** embraces with arms

B. Use words from the list in part A to answer these questions:

1. Which three words describe how someone feels? _____

2. Which three words describe behaviour? _____

3. Find a verb. _____

4. Find a noun. _____

5. Write two sentences using at least two words from the list in each sentence.

    a) _____

       _____

    b) _____

       _____

Learn More

Complete the text with words from the word bank.

Word Bank		
• accountable	• contact	• inevitable
• attachment	• cruel	• issue
• bond	• essential	• required

There will always be a strong _____ between people and animals

because animals are _____ by humans on so many levels, from

food to companionship. Although some of us do manage to live very comfortably

without animal products, most people feel that their use is _____ .

Despite the _____ we have to animals, the way we treat them is

often _____ . The _____ of how we treat them

remains troubling. Some people insist that we cannot avoid mistreating animals on our

farms and in our labs and homes, but is animal cruelty really _____?

Perhaps a bill of rights for animals is needed. Shouldn't we be held _____

for our treatment of them? At the very least, if we witness an animal being abused in

any way, we should definitely _____ our local SPCA.

Your Turn

Write a sentence with each of the words.

1. animal kingdom: _____

2. harvest: _____

3. link: _____

Grammar

Phrasal Verbs

Phrasal verbs are expressions that combine verbs with prepositions or adverbs or both. The new combination usually has a different meaning from the original verb. Phrasal verbs can be either transitive (followed by an object) or intransitive (not followed by an object). Depending on their use, some can be both.

Transitive Expressions: Position of the Object

- If the object is a **noun**, it is usually placed at the end of the expression:

  *The mob pulled down **the statue**.*

- With some expressions, the **noun object** can also be placed after the verb:

  *The mob pulled **the statue** down.*

- If the object is a **pronoun**, it is usually placed after the verb:

  *The mob pulled **it** down.*

- Sometimes an **object pronoun** can be placed at the end of the expression:

  *The police are looking for **them**.*

Common Phrasal Verbs

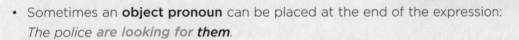

Phrasal Verb	Meaning	Example
back off	leave alone, yield	*I backed off when I realized that she was getting angry.*
call up	telephone	*I called up the radio station to tell them about the protest. (called the radio station up)*
come across	discover	*We came across some documents about the protest.*
find out	discover	*When Jenny found out that Miles had lied, she was very upset.*
get along	have a good relationship	*Ahmer and I don't get along well.*
get away with	go uncaught or unpunished	*Dan got away with breaking the window.*
get over	recover from, overcome	*If we don't succeed, I will never get over it!*
get up	rise from bed	*Jamie gets up late on Sundays.*

→

Phrasal Verb	Meaning	Example
give up	stop trying	*George gave up protesting because he didn't think that he was making a difference.*
go through with	continue	*I was nervous about the show, but I knew that I had to go through with it.*
make up for	compensate for	*I am making up for my mistake by working hard.*
run over	drive across	*My cat ran into the road and was run over by a car.*
shut down	stop or close something	*The police shut down the illegal operation. (shut the illegal operation down)*
stand up for	defend	*Bob Marley wanted us to stand up for our rights.*
stay away from	avoid	*My mother told me to stay away from the protest.*
throw away	get rid of	*Joe has thrown away the documents we needed. (thrown the documents away)*

Frequent Errors

Underline the words that make up the phrasal verbs and correct the errors.

1. When he broke his guitar pick, he threw away it. _____

2. We knew we had to shut up the club. _____

3. He decided to call up me to talk about the problem. _____

4. Every morning I get me early up. _____

5. Ahmer found that Jenny out was stealing from the fund. _____

Practise 1

Complete the sentences with phrasal verbs from the list on pages 61–62.

1. I had _____ early to get to the meeting on time.

2. Mark _____ his anger at me for missing the meeting.

3. I realized that I should _____ trying to make him understand.

4. I _____ him much better now that we are older.

5. He won't let me _____ too much!

6. When I asked him why he was angry, he told me _____ and leave him alone.

Your Turn

Write sentences using the following phrasal verbs.

Phrasal Verbs		
• come across • find out	• make up for • stand up for	• throw away

1. _____

2. _____

3. _____

4. _____

5. _____

Comparing Verb Tenses

This overview of the basic tenses compares how and when they are used.

Simple Present	vs.	Present Continuous
You can use the simple present to describe • a recurring action, habit or routine • a fact • a present state or an opinion *Students often hold sit-ins.*		You can use the present continuous to describe • an action that is happening right now • an ongoing action • a definite plan in the near future *The police are telling students to leave.*

Simple Past	vs.	Past Continuous
You can use the simple past to describe • an action completed in the past • a past state or opinion *I took part in the sit-in against fee increases last year.* When one complete action followed another, use the simple past for both: *The police charged when the students started to throw rocks.*		You can use the past continuous to describe • an ongoing action in the past • an action that was happening at a specific moment in the past *I was walking past the protest at noon.* It can include a shorter, complete action: *While you were watching the protest, I called Sam.* It can occur over the same period as another action: *The police were firing tear gas as the students were running away.*

Future | vs. | Future Continuous

Future

You can use the future to describe
- an intended action
- a future state
- a predictable future event
- a probable future event

*I **will watch** the six o'clock news.*

You can use *to be + going to* and the base form of the main verb to express or ask about a future intention.

*I **am going to watch** the news later.*

Future Continuous

You can use the future continuous to describe
- an action that will be happening at a specific point in the future
- an ongoing action in the future

*I **will be watching** the news at six, so don't call me then.*

Simple Past | vs. | Present Perfect

Simple Past

You can use the simple past to describe
- an action completed in the past
- a past state or opinion

*The police **charged** the crowd.*

It is common to give a specific time with the simple past.

*I **took part** in the sit-in against fee increases last year.*

Present Perfect

You can use the present perfect to describe
- a recently completed action
- an action completed at an unspecified time in the past
- an action that began in the past and is still happening

*Students **have** already **started** to sing.*

The present perfect relates a past event to the present. You often use it with the words *for* and *since*.

*Sam and I **have taken part** in protests **for** three years now. We **have known** each other **since** 2001.*

Simple Past | vs. | Past Perfect

Simple Past

You can use the simple past to describe
- two or more events that happened at the same time in the past.

*Last year the demonstrations **became** violent. Protesters **lit** fires and **threw** rocks.*

Past Perfect

You can use the past perfect to describe
- an action that happened in the past before another past time or event

*The students **had** already **ended** the protest by the time the reporters **arrived**.*

Frequent Errors

For each sentence, circle the verb and identify the tense used. Then write down the verb in the correct tense.

	Tense Used	Correct Verb
1. I am here since six o'clock.		
2. I have been at the music festival last year.		
3. Yesterday I go to the concert.		
4. I work hard until I get a place in the band.		
5. I am practising hard every day.		

Practise 1

Complete the text with the simple present or present continuous form of the verbs in parentheses.

I _____ (to know) that there _____ (to be) many

ways that musicians _____ (to influence) one another. An early

recording of Elvis Presley _____ (to play) as I _____

(to think) about this, and I _____ (to hear) something that

_____ (to catch) my attention. It _____ (to sound)

as though he _____ (to imitate) the popular African-American music

of the 1930s.

Practise 2

Complete the text with the simple past or past continuous form of the verbs in parentheses.

Elvis Presley _____ (to be) the first white musician to record a song

written by an African-American blues singer. This is how it _____

(to happen): Presley _____ (to be) in the recording studio at Sun

Records, in Memphis, Tennessee. The producer, Sam Phillips, _____

(to look) for a new sound. He _____ (to try) to find something that would catch teenagers' attention and make them want to dance. Things

_____ (to work out, negative) very well. Phillips _____

(to be) discouraged and _____ (to go) out for a break. Presley and

his band _____ (to start) fooling around, playing songs that they had

heard on one of the "black" radio stations in Memphis. They _____

(to play) Arthur Crudup's "That's All Right, Mama" when Phillips _____

(to walk) in. Phillips _____ (to love) the new sound. He immediately

_____ (to record) it and _____ (to begin) playing

it on local radio stations. Needless to say, Presley's version, "That's All Right,"

_____ (to become) a huge hit. Rock and roll _____

(to be) born!

Practise 3

Complete the text with the correct future form of the verbs in parentheses: the simple future, the future continuous or both.

In May, our school wind ensemble _____

(to leave) for a music festival in Sherbrooke. We are not ready

yet but we _____ (to be) soon. We

_____ (to perform) three pieces in

front of judges who _____ (to critique + then) our performance.

The ensemble that gets the highest mark _____ (to win) a gold medal.

At the festival, there _____ (to be) about 10 000 musicians

from all over the province. We _____ (to be able) to hear

music everywhere we go, from jazz bands to orchestras, choirs to wind ensembles.

We _____ (to spend) four days surrounded by people who

share our passion. It _____ (to be) great!

Practise 4

Complete the text with the simple past or present perfect form of the verbs in parentheses.

I _____ (to be) here since 9:00 a.m. I _____ (to want)

to meet with the principal but she is not here. Yesterday she _____

(*to cancel*) the rock concert we _____ (*to want*) to hold this weekend. She _____ (to tell) us that we _____ (*to have,
negative*) enough people to act as security. I _____ (*to want*) to tell
her that we _____ (*to change*) our plans since yesterday.
We _____ (*to find*) three more guys to help us out, so now things
should be fine. They _____ (*to work*) at concerts before and
_____ even _____ (*to agree*) to cancel other plans to help us.

Practise 5

**Complete the text with the simple past or past perfect form of the verbs
in parentheses.**

Pete Seeger has finally made peace with the San Diego
School District. In the 1950s, the American government
_____ (*to be*) suspicious of communists.
Seeger, a protest singer, _____ (*to attract*)
attention because of his leftist politics. He _____
(*to be*) under attack because a few months earlier
he _____ (*to refuse*) to answer
questions about his political activities. A school board
in San Diego _____ (*to give*) him an
ultimatum: He _____ (*to have*) to sign
an oath against communism or cancel a concert he
_____ (*to plan*) to give at a local high
school auditorium. Seeger _____ (*to refuse*), but a judge
_____ (*to allow*) the concert to proceed anyway.

   Seeger later _____ (*to say*) that he _____
(*to refuse*) to sign the oath because he _____ (*to want*) to stand up
to the government. In 2009, the school board _____ (*to apologize*)
to Seeger and _____ (*to invite*) him back to perform. They
_____ (*to decide*) to apologize after seeing the music legend—who
_____ (*to continue*) to perform for more than half a century—sing
at President Obama's Inaugural Celebration Concert.

Your Turn

Complete the sentences. Use verbs in the appropriate tense.

1. Every day I _____

_____

2. When I'm 25, _____

_____

3. Before I started high school, _____

_____

4. While I was watching music videos on TV, _____

_____

5. Since 2007, _____

_____

Read and Respond

Music Can't Change the World?

Neil Young, the legendary Canadian protest singer, has a pessimistic message: Music cannot change the world. After more than 40 years in the industry, the once hopeful performer has changed his tune.

5 Young has produced a film of his band's "Freedom of Speech" tour which protests the Iraq war. He said at a press conference promoting the film, "I think that the time when music could change the world is past. I think that it would be very naive to think that in this day and age."

10 Young added, "I think that the world today is a different place, and that it's time for science and physics and spirituality to make a difference in this world and to try to save the planet."

Young said that he called his fellow band members before the tour and told them, "This is all I'm going to do, I won't be doing anything else and I don't want to sing

15 any [. . .] pretty songs. We can sing only about war and politics and the human condition."

"The goal was to stimulate debate among people, and I hope that to some degree the film succeeds in doing that," he said.

→

Comments

Maybe it's true that music doesn't change the world the way we like to think it does. But individual people create change every day: Some can teach, some can protest, others can volunteer time or money. Sometimes a smile is all it takes to
25 make a difference in another person's day. A song certainly might not change the world dramatically overnight, but change has to start somewhere. Musicians can still do their part even if they can't start a revolution. – Optigirl

I don't really know what to think about Young's comments. Maybe he's right. Maybe the time when music could have an effect on the world is over. It's a bit
30 **disheartening** to think that a great song writer and amazing musician like Neil Young feels that the art of song has lost its power to change things. It's sad to say, but perhaps it is time to go beyond singing and look for concrete ways we can change the world. – Mike D

VOCABULARY

disheartening: discouraging

Explore the Text

Before Reading

1. What does *pessimism* mean? Write down your definition and then give an example of a pessimistic idea or attitude.

_____

_____

_____

2. Give examples of musicians who made a difference to the world. How did they do it?

_____

_____

While Reading

3. As you read the comments following the article, write down key ideas and decide if each writer agrees or disagrees with Neil Young.

Optigirl
Agree / Disagree

Mike D
_____
_____
_____
Agree / Disagree

After Reading

4. What is the subject of Neil Young's film?

_____

5. What is the purpose of the concert tour?

_____

6. What reasons does Neil Young give for saying that music can no longer save the world?

_____

_____

_____

7. What kind of music did Young tell the band members they would be playing on the tour?

_____

_____

8. What was the goal of the "Freedom of Speech" tour and film?

_____

Connect With the Text

9. Has listening to music or to a musician ever changed how you think about something? If yes, how?

_____

_____

10. Write your own reader's comment about Neil Young's statements. Use the comments that follow the article as models.

_____

_____

_____

_____

Generalize

11. In your opinion, how could each of the following save the planet?

Science: _____

_____

_____

Spirituality: _____

_____

_____

Vocabulary

Practise

A. Match the words with their definitions.

1. sorrow _____

2. waged _____

3. rioting _____

4. rally _____

5. struggles _____

6. activism _____

7. labour _____

a) difficulties

b) public meeting

c) workforce

d) working for social justice

e) noisy, violent public disorder

f) unhappiness

g) fought

B. Complete the text with words from the word bank.

Word Bank			
• activism	• picket	• sit-ins	• struggles
• civil rights	• rally	• sorrow	• woe
• labour	• rioting		

Throughout history, many issues have pushed people toward _____

—a desire to work for social justice. In this century, two of the biggest issues, along with

anti-war protests, have been _____ and _____

rights. From peaceful _____ to violent _____ ,

people have found ways to make their voices heard. At some point in your own life, you

may find yourself at a _____ holding a _____

sign, because the _____ of a few cause _____ to all.

Learn More

Word Bank
• agreement • complaint • compromise	• concede • conciliation • crisis	• discord • dissent • find the middle ground	• surrender • understanding • unity

A. Write four words from the word bank that refer to conflict.

_____

B. Complete the sentences with words from the word bank.

1. I made a _____ about the way the prisoners were being treated.

2. The feeling of _____ in the meeting made many people uncomfortable.

3. I knew I couldn't win, so I decided to _____ and meet a few of their demands.

4. We tried to _____ to avoid a conflict and make everyone happy.

5. I had no chance of winning, so I knew I had to _____ and let them have their way.

6. After much discussion, the two countries finally reached an _____ about cross-border trade.

Your Turn

Write sentences with the following pairs of words.

1. agreement/crisis _____

_____

2. complaint/find the middle ground _____

_____

3. compromise/discord _____

_____

4. conciliation/surrender _____

_____

5. understanding/unity _____

_____

UNIT 7 — Shakespeare Lives On!

Grammar

Past Participles

- You use **past participles** with the verb *to have* to form the perfect tenses.

  *Lisa has **performed** at the Summer Shakespeare Festival since she graduated from drama school. Ben had already **been** there for two years when Lisa arrived. By the end of the summer, they will have **acted** together in over ten plays.*

- You also use past participles to form the passive voice.
  *The new theatre was **designed** by architect Elisabeth Scott.*

- You can use past participles as adjectives to modify a noun.
  *The **restored** Trinity Church is **known** to Shakespeare's fans around the world.*

- You can use past participles to replace a passive main clause.

  *The actor was **amazed** by the offer. He accepted immediately.* ***Amazed** by the offer, the actor accepted immediately.*

Formation

- Add *ed* to the base form of the regular verbs: *act**ed**, visit**ed**, walk**ed***, etc. If a verb ends in *e*, simply add *d*: *practise = practise**d**, restore = restore**d***, etc.

- Past participles of irregular verbs vary and must be learned or looked up in a dictionary: *been, gone, read, written*, etc. See Common Irregular Verbs on pages 144–147.

Frequent Errors

Circle the past participles and write down the correct forms.

1. Have you finish reading the sonnet?

   _____

2. Coralie said that she wanted to rent the movie *Shakespeare in Love* but it had already been took out. _____

3. The sets were create by a famous designer.

   _____

4. We only arrived at the theatre when the play had begin. _____

5. Both speak and write English have change a lot since Shakespeare's time.

_____ _____ _____

Practise 1

Complete the chart.

Verb	Regular or Irregular	Past Participle
1. bring		
2. dance		
3.		done
4.		fixed
5.		had
6. plant		
7.		said
8. swim		
9.		thought
10. win		

Practise 2

Complete the text with the past participles of the verbs in parentheses.

A Graveyard Story

The gravesite needed to be _____

(*to fix*), but the bones couldn't be

_____ (*to touch*).

This was the problem _____

(*to face*) by officials from the Friend of

Shakespeare's Church group when it was

_____ (*to find*) that

the stones over Shakespeare's grave had

_____ (*to start*) to disintegrate.

Holy Trinity Church in Stratford-upon-Avon was _____ (*to build*)

over 450 years ago and is _____ (*to visit*) by thousands of people

every year. Not only is it the place where Shakespeare was _____
(*to bury*), but he was also baptized _____ (*to baptize*) there
in 1564.

Fixing the flaking stones was only a small part of the general restoration
work _____ (*to require*) for the church. But above the tomb
is _____ (*to engrave*) this chilling verse:

> _____ (*to bless*) be the man that spares these stones,
>
> And _____ (*to curse*) be he that moves my bones.

It is _____ (*to believe*) that this threat was _____
(*to write*) by Shakespeare himself and few people are _____
(*to prepare*) to find out if it will come true.

"Raising over $8 million dollars to repair the church windows is nothing
_____ (*to compare*) to raising the Bard's ghost," said the
project architect.

Your Turn

**A. Write three questions about the gravesite restoration project described
in Practise 2. Use a past participle in each one.**

1. _____

2. _____

3. _____

**B. Write six sentences with a past participle in each one. Underline the past
participles that you use.**

1. _____

2. _____

3. _____

4. _____

5. _____

6. _____

The Active and Passive Voices

The Active Voice

You use the **active voice** when the subject is agent or doer of the action.

Every year the same actor plays the role of Macbeth.

The Passive Voice

You use the **passive voice** when the subject is not the agent or doer of the action, or when the agent is not identified.

Every year the role of Macbeth is played by the same actor.

You can use the passive voice for reports, such as science reports, in which the agent is less important than the facts or analysis. The passive voice is also useful for instructions and rules.

Formation

The passive voice uses the auxiliary verb *to be* with the past participle of the main verb.

Verb Form	Active Voice	Passive Voice
Simple present	*writes*	*is written*
Present continuous	*is writing*	*is being written*
Simple past	*wrote*	*was written*
Past continuous	*was writing*	*was being written*
Present perfect	*has written*	*has been written*
Past perfect	*had written*	*had been written*
Future	*will write*	*will be written*
Present conditional	*would write*	*would be written*
Perfect conditional	*would have written*	*would have been written*
Present infinitive	*to write*	*to be written*
Perfect infinitive	*to have written*	*to have been written*
Present participle/gerund	*writing*	*being written*
Perfect participle	*having written*	*having been written*

To change a sentence from active to passive, you have two options.

1. Move the agent to the end of the sentence and introduce it with the preposition *by*.
   *The new Globe theatre **was inaugurated by** the Queen on June 12 1997.*

2. Eliminate the agent and describe only the action.
   *The new Globe theatre **was inaugurated** on June 12 1997.*

Frequent Errors

Circle the errors in the passive verbs and write the correct forms below.

Has Shakespeare's Theatre (1) Been Find?

LONDON – An important discovery (2) was make in London, England, last week. The foundations of the building, which (3) was knowed as The Theatre, (4) was uncovered during excavations for a new office building. It (5) is thinked to be the place where plays such as *The Merchant of Venice* and *Romeo and Juliet* (6) was performed. In fact, the stage (7) may been graced by Shakespeare himself.

The Theatre (8) was builded in 1576 and was one of three theatres (9) use by Shakespeare's company. Another Shakespearean theatre, The Rose, (10) has was discovered in 1989. Archeologists (11) was summon to the site to ensure that nothing (12) was damage.

1. _____   7. _____
2. _____   8. _____
3. _____   9. _____
4. _____   10. _____
5. _____   11. _____
6. _____   12. _____

Practise

Complete the sentences with the passive form of the verbs in parentheses.

When Alicia went to Stratford-upon-Avon, she _____ (*to delight*) by the beauty and charm of the little village. Her class spent a week on a tour that _____ (*to organize*) by an educational travel company. They began their visit to Stratford by crossing an ancient bridge over the River Avon that _____ (*to build*) in the 1600s. Then they went to

Henley Street to visit the house where Shakespeare _____

(*to be born*), which _____ (*to restore*) to its original state.

They also visited Anne Hathaway's house, which _____

(*to live*) in by the Hathaway family until 1892.

   When Alicia and her classmates came back, a special evening _____

(*to plan*) for the other students and members of the community. They complained,

however, that the principal _____ (*to give*, negative) them

enough time to prepare,

so the presentation was postponed and a new date _____

(*to set*). A photo display _____ (*to set up*) in the auditorium

and a multi-media presentation _____ (*to show*).

Your Turn

**Write six questions to ask Alicia about her trip and what she learned. Write three
questions in the active voice and three in the passive voice.**

_____

_____

_____

_____

_____

_____

Read and Respond

Shakespeare Portrait Unveiled

By Gregory Katz

LONDON – Scholars studying the life and times of William Shakespeare unveiled a portrait today believed to be the only authentic image of the Bard painted during his lifetime.

Experts at the Shakespeare Birthplace Trust think the painting was used as the basis for the image of Shakespeare that graces the cover of the First Folio collection of his plays. Paul Edmondson, the group's director of learning, said it was also used as a basis for the famous portrait of the playwright that hangs in the Folger Shakespeare Library in Washington.

"What makes it so important is that it's a portrait of William Shakespeare made during his lifetime," he said. "We think it was painted in 1610 and several copies of it were made early on, including the engraving. So our portrait is the primary version of one of the greatest portraits of Shakespeare."

The other images were all made after Shakespeare's death in 1616, he said, making the newly unveiled portrait unique.

Mr. Edmondson said experts are confident that the handsome, bearded man in the portrait is the author of some of the most enduring words ever written in the English language.

"We're 90 per cent sure that it's Shakespeare," he said. "You'll never be entirely certain. There will always be voices of dissent."

He said scholars are convinced it is Shakespeare because so many copies of the painting were made, including the one at the Folger, and because the painting was handed down through the generations along with a portrait of the Earl of Southampton, Shakespeare's main patron.

He said the portrait had long been part of the Cobbe collection owned by the Cobbe family, but had not been connected to Shakespeare until 2006, when one of the family members saw the Folger Shakespeare painting on display at a travelling exhibition in London and realized the similarity between the two.

The disclosure was made on a bumper day for Shakespeare fans and devotees throughout the world: the Museum of London also announced that the foundations of the theatre where Shakespeare's plays were performed, and where he himself performed as an actor, had been found in Hackney on the eastern outskirts of London.

The museum's archaeologists had also found a piece of pottery with an image of a man who resembles Shakespeare, said spokesperson Tim Morley.

"We are 99 per cent certain this is the theatre, it's in the right place and the brickwork is the right age," he said.

→

Museum officials said the rudimentary playhouse, called the Theatre, was built in 1576 by James Burbage. The site, where Shakespeare performed from 1594 to 1597, now houses an abandoned warehouse. Experts believe *Romeo and Juliet* was performed there.

Officials hope to build a small new theatre on the site.

Source: Associated Press, March 9, 2009

Explore the Text

Before Reading

1. Have you ever seen any portraits of Shakespeare? Where were they?

   _____

2. List all the Shakespearean plays that you know.

   _____

   _____

   _____

   _____

3. Match the words with their synonyms.

   1. bumper _____   **a)** basic

   2. dissent _____   **b)** disagreement

   3. enduring _____   **c)** drawing

   4. engraving _____   **d)** long-lasting

   5. handed down _____   **e)** given

   6. handsome _____   **f)** good-looking

   7. outskirts _____   **g)** representative

   8. rudimentary _____   **h)** surrounding area

   9. spokesperson _____   **i)** unusually large/full

   10. unveiled _____   **j)** uncovered

While Reading

4. Using information from the text on pages 79–80, place the main events in the history of the portrait in chronological order.

   _____   A member of the Cobbe family saw the Folger portrait in 2006.

   _____   Copies of the portrait were made.

_____ He realized that their portrait was similar.

_____ It was also used as the inspiration for the portrait that hangs in the Folger Shakespeare Library in Washington.

_____ It was handed down through the generations.

_____ Other portraits were painted after Shakespeare's death in 1616.

_____ The cover of the first folio collection was based on it.

_____ The discovery of the painting and the finding of the Theatre were announced at the same time.

_____ The portrait was painted in 1610.

_____ The portrait was part of the Cobbe family collection.

After Reading

5. Indicate if the following sentences are true (T) or false (F). Correct the false answers.

Sentence	True or False	Correction
1. The engraving for Shakespeare's first book cover was based on the painting.	_____	_____ _____ _____
2. Experts think that this is one more authentic painting of Shakespeare.	_____	_____ _____ _____
3. The painting was done at the beginning of the 1600s.	_____	_____ _____ _____
4. Everyone agrees that this is probably a portrait of Shakespeare.	_____	_____ _____ _____
5. The Cobbes did not know that the portrait was of Shakespeare.	_____	_____ _____ _____

Connect With the Text

6. Why do you think people are so fascinated by the discovery of Shakespearean artifacts? What do you think about his popularity? Give reasons for your answers.

_____

_____

_____

_____

_____

Generalize

7. With which French author would you compare Shakespeare? Explain your answer.

_____

_____

_____

_____

_____

8. Do you think that society exaggerates the importance of such figures? Explain the criteria you would use to choose the members of a Literary Hall of Fame.

_____

_____

_____

_____

_____

_____

9. Which writer do you think should be in a Literary Hall of Fame? Using the criteria you suggested in Question 9, write a short paragraph to propose her or him. Support your proposal with examples.

_____

_____

_____

_____

_____

_____

Vocabulary

Practise 1

Complete the sentences with words from the word bank.

Word Bank
• grammar school   • outraged   • thatched
• inherited   • royalties   • the Bard
• kingdom   • run away

1. Shakespeare's nickname is _____ .

2. When King Lear decides to give up his _____ , he calls his daughters together to decide who will take his place.

3. Many homes in Shakespeare's day had _____ roofs.

4. Macbeth is now available on the Internet for free. No one receives

   _____ .

5. Claudius is _____ by Hamlet's mad behaviour.

6. When Shakespeare was a boy, he went to _____ to learn Latin, grammar, logic, rhetoric and literary style.

7. Shakespeare's elder daughter, Susanna, _____ his best bed.

8. Romeo and Juliet plan to _____ but everything goes wrong.

Practise 2

Complete the sentences with words from the word bank.

Word Bank	
• chuckle	• cowardice
• cobbled	• grief

1. In medieval times, roads were often paved with round stones _____ .

2. King Lear died from extreme sadness _____ when his daughter Cordelia was murdered.

3. Macbeth's wife accused him of fear and weakness _____ when he refused to kill the king.

4. Shakespeare would laugh _____ if he heard how his invented words are part of our everyday vocabulary.

Learn More

A. Match the words with their definitions.

1. lead role _____
2. performance _____
3. play _____
4. playbill _____
5. playwright _____
6. part _____
7. Shakespearean _____
8. supporting actor _____
9. usher _____

a) Story in dramatic form
b) Actor who plays a secondary role
c) Adjective relating to Shakespeare
d) Document advertising a play
e) Role
f) Person who escorts people to their places
g) Person who has the main role
h) Person who writes dramatic presentations
i) Presentation of a piece of theatre or music

B. Read the following pairs of words. Indicate if they are synonyms or antonyms. Write a sentence to illustrate each pair.

Word Pair	Synonym	Antonym	Example
1. comic relief – tragedy			_____
2. lead role – supporting role			_____
3. performance – play			_____
4. storyline – plot			_____
5. theatregoer – playwright			_____

Your Turn

Write a paragraph about your experience of going to a play. Use at least five of the words listed in A above. Underline these words in your text.

_____
_____
_____
_____
_____

When Human Rights Go Wrong

Grammar

Adverbs and Their Position

You use adverbs to add meaning by describing, intensifying or clarifying what you say or write. Adverbs can modify a verb, an adjective, another adverb or a whole sentence.

Formation

- Some adverbs have the same form as adjectives: *fast, hard, early, late, much, enough*, etc.
- Many adverbs are formed by adding *ly* to an adjective: *smartly, quickly, loudly, really, independently, extremely*, etc.

Position

- An adverb that modifies a verb can follow or precede it, depending on the type of adverb and the emphasis desired.

  *Migrant workers **work hard** and **often earn** very little.*

- An adverb that modifies an adjective or another adverb usually precedes it.

  *I was **very** angry that they were treated **so** badly.*

Position	Adverbs by Type	Examples
At the beginning or end of a sentence or clause	**Time:** *at once, yet, before, since, soon, eventually, lately, now, recently*	*Now is the time for action!* *He will leave **eventually**.*
	Manner: *somehow, anyway*	*We'll get it done **somehow**.*
	Place/Direction: *anywhere, far, away, somewhere, nowhere*	*She is going **away**.* ***Anywhere** we go is fine with me.*
	Frequency: *once, sometimes, often, occasionally, usually*	***Once** I met the Prime Minister.* ***Occasionally**, he writes me a letter.*
After the verb *to be* After an auxiliary verb Before a main verb	**Time:** *soon, eventually, lately, now, recently, still, always*	*Nash is **always** hungry.* *He is **still** working on his essay.*
	Frequency: *always, never, often, sometimes, once, repeatedly, usually*	*I **always** organize my ideas before I write.*
	Certainty: *actually, definitely, probably, perhaps, surely, frankly, totally*	*We **definitely** need a new office.*
	Degree: *almost, barely, enough, just, hardly, nearly*	*I **almost** forgot to call you about the meeting.*
	Manner: *reluctantly, quickly*	*He **quickly** took photos of the people.*

Position	Adverbs by Type	Examples
After a verb	**Place/Direction:** *up, down, there, everywhere, west, away, across*	He walked **down** to the shore.
	Manner: *sadly, angrily, bravely, hard, happily, tirelessly, well, softly, carefully*	She worked **tirelessly** all night.
Before another adverb or an adjective	**Degree:** *almost, nearly, really, painfully, only, completely, absolutely, very, much, too, fairly*	You are **absolutely** wrong about him. It is a **fairly** difficult issue to discuss in an hour.
At the end of a sentence or clause	**Manner:** *well*	She knows that area **well**.
	Time: *early, immediately, late, yet*	We had to leave the meeting **early**. I haven't called him **yet**.

Note: Do not place an adverb between a verb and its direct object.
~~You speak well English~~.

Frequent Errors

Underline the adverbs and circle the words they modify. Rewrite the sentences with the verbs and adverbs in the correct order.

1. I feel always sad when I hear about victims of human rights abuse.

_____

2. Caroline understands the problems well of migrant workers.

_____

3. People are punished still for expressing their political views.

_____

4. We very are fortunate to live in a country where freely we can express our opinions.

_____

_____

Practise 1

Use the adverbs in parentheses to complete the sentences. Rewrite the sentences with the adverbs in the correct position.

1. People have the right to life, liberty and security. (*everywhere*)

_____

2. All men and women deserve to be treated equally. (*definitely*)

_____

_____

3. People's rights are violated. (*constantly, unfortunately*)

_____

_____

4. It makes me angry when I hear about situations where human rights are not respected. (*extremely*)

_____

_____

5. Many organizations work to solve problems around the world. (*hard*)

_____

6. Canada has been accused of abusing human rights. (*even*)

_____

Practise 2

Complete the text with appropriate adverbs from the word bank.

Word Bank		
• around	• harder	• since
• constantly	• nearly	• unfortunately
• everywhere	• properly	

_____ , in some countries, children

live in the worst conditions imaginable. UNICEF (the

United Nations Children's Fund) is an organization that

is _____ working to defend children's rights. It was created after

World War II to help children in Europe. _____ 1946, UNICEF

has been active in protecting children _____ the world. Today,

UNICEF is present in _____ every country and is working

_____ than ever before. UNICEF's mission is to help meet the basic

needs of children _____ and ensure that they are treated

_____ .

Your Turn

Write a few sentences to share your opinion about organizations like UNICEF. Include at least five adverbs. Underline the adverbs you use.

_____

_____

_____

_____

Gerunds and Full Infinitives

Gerunds and **full infinitives** are verb forms that you use like nouns.

Gerunds

- You can use a gerund as **the subject** of a sentence.
  Bullying is a problem in many schools.

- You can use a gerund as **the object** of a verb or **after a preposition**.
  *Marc likes **listening** to protest songs. He's looking forward to **hearing** Eminem's new CD.*

- Gerunds are also used **in compound words** to indicate purpose: *diving* board, *running* shoes, *swimming* pool, *walking* stick.

Formation

- Add *ing* to the base form of the verb: *rain**ing**, scream**ing**, sing**ing**, try**ing**, walk**ing**.*
- If a verb ends in *e*, the e is dropped: *to make = mak**ing**, to write = writ**ing**.*
- If a verb ends in a consonant preceded by a single vowel, the consonant is usually doubled before adding *ing*: *to let = lett**ing**, to swim = swim**ming**.*

Full Infinitives

- You can use a full infinitive as **the subject** of a sentence:
  *To **ignore** human rights abuse is unacceptable.*

- You can use a full infinitive as the **object** of a verb.
  *I wanted **to participate** in the protest but my father told me **to stay away**.*

- You can also use a full infinitive after certain adjectives, such as *happy, lucky, sad, sorry,* and after certain nouns, such as *ability, decision, plan, refusal.*
  *I was so **sad** to see the photos of the refugee camp.*
  *Her **plan** to go to the anti-war concert fell through.*

  Reminder: Do not mix gerunds and infinitives in the same sentence.
  ***Watching** that video and **hearing** the children cry made me angry.*
  (**not** *Watching that video and to hear the children . . .*)

  *She volunteered **to collect** money and **to arrange** a fund-raising concert.*
  (**not** *She volunteered to collect money and arranging a fund-raising concert.*

- A gerund (not a full infinitive) follows a preposition.
  *Let's find out about **raising** money for landmine victims.*
  (**not** *Let's find out about to raise.*)

→ LEARN MORE

- Gerunds are often used on signs to indicate that an action is not permitted.
  *No **hunting**   No **smoking** allowed   No **loitering***

- Some verbs can be followed by an infinitive or a gerund: *to allow, to begin, to continue, to forget, to hate, to like, to love, to mean, to need, to prefer, to regret, to remember, to start, to try.*

- Some verbs can be followed only by a gerund: *to admit, to avoid, to consider, to defend, to deny, to enjoy, to finish, to imagine, to mind, to practise, to risk, to suggest.*

- Some verbs can be followed only by a full infinitive: *to agree, to ask, to choose, to decide, to expect, to hope, to learn, to plan, to promise, to seem, to want, to wish.*

Frequent Errors

Circle the verb errors in the sentences and write down the correct form.

1. To learn and reading about organizations like UNICEF is very interesting.

_____

2. However, I don't enjoy to talk about children who are suffering.

_____

3. Now, I can't avoid to think about victims of human rights abuse.

_____

4. After to hear about how I can help, I want to do something making a difference.

_____

5. I decided raising money for street kids in Montréal.

_____

Practise 1

Complete the sentences with the gerund or full infinitive of the verbs in parentheses.

1. Everyone should do his or her part _____ (*to defend*) human rights.

2. We want _____ (*to put*) an end to human rights abuse.

3. _____ (*to join*) an organization like Amnesty International is a good way to start.

4. _____ (*to send*) letters is one small way that we can help political prisoners.

5. _____ (*to participate*) in a letter-writing campaign is easy to do and helps _____ (*to make*) a difference in the world.

6. It is possible for everyone _____ (*to take*) action.

7. If each person does something small, change will start _____ (*to happen*).

Practise 2

Complete the text with the gerund or full infinitive of the verbs in parentheses.

_____ (*to bully*) someone is a violation of human rights. Some students in our school were victims of _____ (*to bully*) this week and things ended very badly. Students started _____ (*to insult*) each other and then a fight broke out. We could hear people _____ (*to shout*) and then everyone started _____ (*to run*) toward the scene of the fight. One student was seriously injured. Now, the students regret _____ (*to act*) the way they did. We all hope that they have learned a lesson.

Your Turn

Complete the sentences. Use the gerund or full infinitive form of the verbs in parentheses.

1. I don't like . . . (*to talk*)

_____

2. My objective . . . (*to run*)

_____

3. For many years, people . . . (*to defend*)

_____

4. It is unfortunate . . . (*to suffer*)

_____

5. At first, I was nervous . . . (*to participate*)

_____

Read and Respond

A Senseless Slaughter

by Kevin Dougherty

KUUJJUAQ – One by one, elderly Inuit approached the microphone in the Kuujjuaq town hall last week and vented their anger at the killing of their dogs by Mounties and the Sûreté du Québec half a century ago.

Speaking in the soft guttural bursts of Inuktitut, after the premiere of the documentary *Echo of the Last Howl,* they talked about the killings, singly or in groups, of nearly 20 000 huskies— quimmiq, as the Inuit call them.

Inuit credit the dogs for their survival in severe Arctic conditions. When the dogs were killed by the police in the 1950s and 1960s, the effect on their lifestyle was devastating, they say. Today, there are only about 290 of the dogs left in Canada.

"My father lost all his dogs," said one man, repeating a common theme. Police hunted down dogs hidden under houses or on islands away from built-up areas.

"They were my means of survival," said Eli Elijassiapik, another hunter from Inukjuaq on Hudson Bay. "We have not had one word of explanation from the government."

The police admit that dogs were killed, saying they were strays, diseased or a danger to humans, but deny a systematic slaughter took place. The Inuit say that dogs were shot for no reason.

The 10 000 Inuit living here in Nunavik and the 22 500 Inuit in the federal Arctic territory of Nunavut want a public inquiry into the dog killings. They also want an apology and compensation—possibly as subsidies to offset the $1.29-a-litre price of gas for their snowmobiles and the high cost of perishable food in the north.

Fifty years ago, police killing the dogs met little resistance. In Kuujjuaq last week, the old hunters used the Inuktitut term *qaalunate* to describe the respect, deference, even fear of the white authorities who controlled their lives back then. "We were very intimidated by the white men," they explained.

→

Québec's Inuit live in 14 coastal settlements, from Ungava Bay to Hudson Bay, where once qimmiq provided transportation and security, warning of **prowling** polar bears, while Inuit families slept in their igloos. In packs, the dogs attacked bears and caribou, and they sniffed out seals under sea ice. They rescued people and took their masters home in the worst blizzards.

Without dogs, the Inuit had no means of transportation and no **livelihood**, they say. They came to rely on the government for food and shelter.

According to a 2004 Université Laval study, 55 per cent of households in Nunavik live below the poverty line. To cut costs, a family will cut off its telephone or satellite television service.

"It is good to have," said Paulusie Qautsiaq, recounting that his family appreciates satellite television. When the Qautsiaqs cancelled the service to save money, they discovered a new dependency.

Source: Gazette Québec Bureau.

"Our children and our grandchildren are afraid when there is nothing to watch," Qautsiaq said.

VOCABULARY

deference: deep respect and submission
diseased: sick
guttural: coming from the throat
livelihood: financial support
Mounties: Royal Canadian Mounted Police
prowling: moving slowly to find something to eat
stray: animal without an owner

Explore the Text

Before Reading

1. Read the title of the news article and look at the pictures. What do you think the text is about?

_____

2. What do you know about life in the northern regions of Québec?

_____

While Reading

3. Underline all the words in Inuktitut, the Inuit language in the text. Choose five of the words and write them in the table below. Write down the meaning of each word.

Word in Inuktitut	Meaning
Kuujjuaq	
Inuktitut	

Word in Inuktitut	Meaning
Quimmiq	
Inuit	
Inukjuaq	
Nunavik	
Nunavut	
Qaalunate	
Ungava (Bay)	

After Reading

4. Check your prediction from Question 1. What is the topic of this text?

_____

5. What reasons were given for the slaughter of the animals?

_____

6. Why didn't the Inuit protest when this event occurred 50 years ago?

_____

_____

7. How did the slaughter of the husky dogs affect the Inuit lifestyle?

_____

_____

_____

8. In what ways did the dogs provide security for the Inuit people?

_____

_____

_____

Connect With the Text

9. What have you learned about life in the North?

_____

_____

_____

10. What do you think Paulusie Qautsiaq means when he says, "Our children and our grandchildren are afraid when there is nothing to watch"?

_____

_____

11. The news article was published following the premiere of the documentary *Echo of the Last Howl.* After reading the text, would you be interested in viewing the film? Explain your answer.

_____

_____

Generalize

12. The news article refers to the slaughter of 20 000 husky dogs. What are other examples of mass killings of humans or animals that have occurred throughout history?

_____

_____

13. Write a paragraph to explain how the event described in the article on pages 91–92 represents human rights abuse. Use information from the text to support your ideas.

_____

_____

_____

_____

_____

Vocabulary

Practise

Replace the highlighted words in the text with words from the word bank.

Word Bank		
• apartheid	• dismantle	• nor
• compromise	• no matter	• welfare

Racial segregation _____ in South Africa was introduced as law in 1948. Nelson Mandela is highly respected by people all around the world because of his efforts to break down _____ racial segregation in his country. Mandela was concerned with the well-being _____ of all citizens. Mandela was in prison for 27 years. However, he would not give up _____ his political beliefs neither _____ would he accept certain offers in exchange for personal freedom. He was willing to stand up for his beliefs, regardless of _____ what he would have to suffer.

Learn More

A. Match each of the following words with its definition. Then use each word in a sentence.

1. just _____

2. resolution _____

3. responsibility _____

4. warranted _____

a) conclusion

b) deserved

c) duty

d) fair

1. _____

2. _____

3. _____

4. _____

B. Choose four of the following words: *acquittal, conviction, duty, pardon, quandary, reprieve.* **Create word pyramids with the four words. Use the model for help.**

Model

predicament
(Word)

solution   success
(Two antonyms)

circumstance   emergency   quandary
(Three synonyms)

difficult   unfortunate   challenging   unpleasant
(Four words related to the word)

The students wondered how they got themselves into this predicament.
(A sentence using the word)

Word Pyramid 1

_____
(Word)

_____-_____
(Two antonyms)

_____ _____ _____
(Three synonyms)

_____ _____ _____ _____
(Four words related to the word)

_____
(A sentence using the word)

Word Pyramid 2

```
                    _____
                         (Word)
              _____   _____
                    (Two antonyms)
        _____  _____  _____
                   (Three synonyms)
     _____  _____  _____  _____
              (Four words related to the word)
     _____
               (A sentence using the word)
```

Word Pyramid 3

```
                    _____
                         (Word)
              _____   _____
                    (Two antonyms)
        _____  _____  _____
                   (Three synonyms)
     _____  _____  _____  _____
              (Four words related to the word)
     _____
               (A sentence using the word)
```

Word Pyramid 4

```
                    _____
                         (Word)
              _____   _____
                    (Two antonyms)
        _____  _____  _____
                   (Three synonyms)
     _____  _____  _____  _____
              (Four words related to the word)
     _____
               (A sentence using the word)
```

Grammar

The Perfect Conditional

You can use the **perfect conditional** to describe

- an unreal past event   *If we had known about that program, we would have applied.*
- a probable past event   *The recruiters should have arrived by now.*
- a possible past event   *The storm could have delayed them.*
- advice about a past event   *You should have taken the train.*

Formation

Affirmative	Negative*	Interrogative
I, You, He/She/It, We, They would have called.	*I, You, He/She/It, We, They would not have called.*	*Would I, you, he/she/it, we, they have called?*
I, You, He/She/It, We, They should have called.	*I, You, He/She/It, We, They should not have called.*	*Should I, you, he/she/it, we, they have called?*
I, You, He/She/It, We, They could have called.	*I, You, He/She/It, We, They could not have called.*	*Could I, you, he/she/it, we, they have called?*

* In everyday English, you can use the contracted form of *would not* (*wouldn't*), *should not* (*shouldn't*) or *could not* (*couldn't*).

Affirmative: Use *would/should/could have* and the past participle of the main verb.

Negative: Use *would/should/could not have* and the past participle of the main verb.

Interrogative: To ask a question, start with the modal auxiliary *would/should/could*, followed by the subject, *have,* and the past participle of the main verb.

→ LEARN MORE

The present conditional and perfect conditional are often used in conditional sentences* to describe the potential result of a condition. Review the differences between the present conditional and the perfect conditional.

The Present Conditional	If-clause	Main clause
To refer to present or future conditions that could still be fulfilled but are improbable: *Yan would go to film school in New York if he saved $40 000.*	simple past	present conditional
To indicate that events in the main clause are more or less probable, use the modal auxiliaries *could* or *should* to form the present conditional. *If Yan saves enough money, he should go to film school.*	simple present	present conditional

* For more information on conditional sentences, see page 40.

The Perfect Conditional	If-clause	Main clause
To indicate a probable past event: *Yan's acceptance letter should have arrived this morning, if the mail was delivered.*	simple past	perfect conditional
To refer to past conditions that did not happen: *If Yan had saved $40 000, he would have gone to film school in New York.*	past perfect	perfect conditional
You can use *could* or *might* instead of *would* in the main clause: *Yan's film might have won the prize if he had had more time to work on it.* You can also use *could have* in the if-clause: *If they could have taken time off work, Yan's parents would have come to the screening.*		

Frequent Errors

Practise your editing skills. Read the text below and underline the error in the use of the perfect conditional. Write the correction above the line.

My uncle commented once: "If I would have see myself twenty years later, I would lived life differently." Now that I am older, I see why he said that! I often wonder about the choices I've made. If I had spent a year in Japan, should I be living in Québec today? If I hadn't go to Berlin to be an au pair, would I have learned German? Should I had stayed in Europe and married that biologist from Lisbon? If I had stayed in Ottawa after university and worked on Parliament Hill, could I became an interpreter for the United Nations like Vikram? If I could have seen into the future, I might became a completely different person!

Practise 1

Complete the sentences with the appropriate form of the verbs in parentheses.

1. If Kendra had gone to Italy, she _____ (*to study*) in Florence.

2. Do you think the Nesrallahs _____ (*to sell*) their car if they had moved downtown?

3. Jamal and Eric _____ (*to adopt*) a child from each continent if they could have!

4. If Paola had bought her own turntables, she _____ (*to become*) a DJ by now.

5. If he hadn't played in the soccer tournament in Brazil, Jussi _____

_____ (*to meet*, negative) the talent scout.

Practise 2

Review the present conditional and the perfect conditional. Complete the sentences correctly.

1. If Petra had made an effort, _____

    a) she will find a job. **b)** she would find a job. **c)** she could have found a job.

2. If Adrian had married his girlfriend, _____

    a) he should have moved to Tulsa with her. **b)** he will move to Tulsa with her.
    c) he would have moved to Tulsa with her.

3. If Takeshi volunteered in Benin, _____

    a) he could also visit Ghana and Togo. **b)** he will also visit Ghana and Togo.
    c) he would have also visited Ghana and Togo.

4. If Liang hadn't entered law school, _____

    a) he might not become a judge. **b)** he might not have become a judge.
    c) he should not have become a judge.

5. If Janice passes her driving exam, _____

    a) she should buy a motorbike. **b)** she could have bought a motorbike.
    c) she should have bought a motorbike.

Your Turn

Life is a series of causes and effects. Think of someone you know. Then write about five events in that person's life that show cause and effect. Use the perfect conditional.

_____

_____

_____

_____

_____

_____

The Future Perfect

You can use the **future perfect** to describe an action that will occur in the future before some other future event.

By thirty-five, I will have become a famous chef with my own restaurant.

My friends will have started their own surfing school in 10 years.

By the time we have our 20-year reunion, we'll have changed a lot.

Formation

Affirmative*	Negative*	Interrogative
I, You, He/She/It, We, They **will have** *graduated.*	*I, You, He/She/It, We, They* **will not have** *graduated.*	*Will I, you, he/she/it, we, they* **have** *graduated?*

* In everyday English, use the contracted form of the *will* (*'ll*) and *will not* (*won't*).

Affirmative: Use *will have* (the future of the auxiliary verb *to have*) and the past participle of the main verb.

Negative: Use *will not have* with the past participle of the main verb.

Interrogative: To ask a question, start with the auxiliary *will*, followed by the subject, *have*, and the past participle of the main verb.

Time markers: *by a certain date* (e.g. *by Friday, by next year, by the end of January*), *by that time, by then, when,* etc.

Frequent Errors

Circle the future perfect errors in the following sentences. Then rewrite the sentences correctly.

1. Our classmates will have reach middle age in 20 years!

_____

2. By that time, I hope that people will switched to hybrid cars.

_____

3. I'm afraid that the pollution problem not will have been solve.

_____

4. Will have schools replace teachers with computers by 2030?

_____

5. By the time we have our own children, education has changed a lot.

_____

Practise 1

Circle the verb in the future perfect. Underline the time clue.

1. Lara hopes that she will have signed a record deal by the time she is 25.

2. In five years, Alain will have moved to Rimouski.

3. Keisha will have graduated from medical school as a surgeon in 15 years.

4. By next summer, Danny will have married the love of his life.

5. By the time Alex is 35, she will have published her first book.

6. By then, Wayson will have launched his dance career in Europe.

Practise 2

Futurists make the following predictions about the world in 2030. Complete the predictions with the future perfect of the verbs in parentheses.

1. Access to electricity _____
   (*to spread*) to 83% of the world by 2030.

2. By then, half the world's population

   _____ (*to face*) serious
   water shortages.

3. By 2030, 60% of the global population

   _____ (*to move*) to urban
   centres.

4. The race for genetic enhancement _____ (*to reach*) the
   same level of importance as the space race had in the 20th century.

5. A new generation of students _____ (*to choose*)
   increasingly specialized fields like sustainable business and nanotechnology.

6. Rapid changes in work-related technologies _____
   (*to require*) workers to constantly retrain for their jobs.

7. By then, the world's legal systems _____ (*to be*)
   networked.

8. Bicycles _____ (*to replace*) the car as the primary
   means of transportation.

9. The United States and Iran _____ (*to become*) allies.

10. By 2030, people _____ (*to get*) used to having their
    speech and actions recorded at all times.

Your Turn

Write six predictions about your life, using the future perfect: two in the affirmative, two using the negative and two using the interrogative.

1. _____

2. _____

3. _____

4. _____

5. _____

6. _____

Read and Respond

Back to the Future

What will the future bring? People just can't stop asking that question. Some bold thinkers try answering it, too.

by Terri L. Jones

Home, Sweet Robot

In the 1950s, Ray Bradbury wrote a book called *The Martian Chronicles*. It describes a house that talks. From inside the walls, a voice tells people when to get out of bed. It also tells them whose birthday it is and how to dress.

In Bradbury's house of the future, there is a robot for every chore. One robot cooks while other robots set the table and wash the dishes. Tiny mice-like robots scurry around vacuuming the floor. Some of Bradbury's predictions came true. Today, robots are on the job in many places. They vacuum floors. They cook meals. They even build cars and explore outer space.

Cities in Space

Some predictions that were made in the 1950s were out of this world. Writers, scientists, and artists imagined whole cities in space. Some thought that by the early 1990s, earthlings would live on the Moon. Can you imagine sitting under a glass dome, watching Earth rise and set?

How would people grow fruits and vegetables in space? Simple. They'd use hydroponics, which is a well-known way to grow plants without soil. How would they heat their buildings? Energy from the sun would supply all their power.

These ideas weren't so crazy. Today, many homes on Earth use solar power. Even some experimental cars and planes run on energy from the sun. Astronauts live for months on the International Space Station. However, the space city of people's imagination is still many years away.

Present + Possible = Future

The dreamers of the 1950s also had ideas about how people might communicate.

One idea turned up in the *Dick Tracy* comic strip. Tracy was a tough, smart detective. He had a special way of staying in touch with people. On his wrist, Tracy wore an amazing watch. It had a telephone that he could use anywhere. Even better, it had a two-way television. This meant he could see people while he was talking to them.

The two parts of Tracy's watch—telephone and television—existed in the 1950s. Yet it took an artist to put them together in a new way. Slowly, real life caught up with the comics. Today, people have cellphones. Some are even videophones. People also use webcams to see each other while they "talk" over the Internet. As *Dick Tracy* predicted, pieces of what was the present came together later in the future.

Up, Up, But Not Away

Some people don't stop at imagining the future. They start building it. That happened when people wanted better ways to get around. Take the jetpack. It's a backpack that carries a small rocket engine. You put it on, rev it up, and soar. No need to ask for a ride to school or wait for the bus. Real life turned out to be more complicated.

Source: *National Geographic* April 2009

For starters, jetpacks can't carry much fuel. So the average trip is maybe half a minute. Then there are problems with safety. Jetpack fuel can be dangerous stuff. It heats up to about 700 degrees Celsius. The roaring engine can also damage your hearing.

Someday, a clever inventor may come up with a jetpack that truly takes off. It may be a while, though. So you'd better hold on to your bus pass.

Getting From Here to There

Another invention that flew was the Aerocar. It was a flying car with folding wings. A silly idea, right? But wait! An Aerocar was built in 1949. In fact, six of them were built over the next 10 years. They really worked! Still, the idea never caught on. Maybe Aerocars were too hard to land in the driveway.

Fast Forward

Think about your future and start dreaming. Will you get to work with a jetpack? Will you download digital books straight into your brain? Invisibility suits and underwater cities are just two things that may be possible. What else? Think big. Think fantastic! The future is yours to invent.

Explore the Text

Before Reading

1. What books about the future have you already read?

_____

_____

2. Read the title of the article on page 102. What do you think the text will be about?

_____

_____

3. Find the following words in the text. Look up the words in a dictionary and write the definitions.

Word	What It Means
scurry	
earthlings	
hydroponics	
turned up	
staying in touch	
caught up	
rev it up	
soar	
roaring	

While Reading

4. Read the following statements. Circle **T** if the text confirms the statement and **F** if the text refutes the statement. Correct the false answers.

a)	Ray Bradbury described a house of the future that has TVs that tell people when to get up, what to wear and when people's birthdays are. _____	T	F
b)	Robots are only used in industrial settings today. _____	T	F
c)	People predicted solar power in the 1950s. _____	T	F
d)	People in the 1950s thought that by 2009 earthlings would live on the Moon. _____	T	F

e)	Hydroponics is a way to cultivate vegetables using minimal soil. _____	T	F
f)	International astronauts are building space cities. _____	T	F
g)	Dick Tracy, a cartoon detective, used the forerunner of a cellphone. _____	T	F
h)	The jetpack was to be used to propel vehicles. _____	T	F
i)	A disadvantage of the jetpack is the speed of the engine. _____	T	F
j)	The first Aerocar was invented in the 1940s. _____	T	F

After Reading

5. Which predictions of the 1950s have actually come true?

_____

_____

Connect With the Text

6. Complete the sentences below.

a) If Ray Bradbury hadn't written *The Martian Chronicles* . . .

_____

_____

b) If Dick Tracy hadn't had a videophone watch . . .

_____

_____

c) If scientists had found a way to build space cities . . .

_____

_____

d) If a clever inventor had found a way to make jetpacks feasible . . .

_____

_____

7. Which invention mentioned in this article do you think will most likely exist in 50 years? Explain why.

_____

_____

_____

8. In what ways do you think downloading digital books directly into your brain would be advantageous for students of the future? Can you think of any disadvantages?

_____

_____

_____

9. As Raymond Bradbury predicted, we now have robots that cook and clean. Robots also build cars and explore outer space. As robot technology improves, what kind of effect do you think this will have on your employment opportunities in the future? Do you think there will be fewer jobs for people? Why or why not?

_____

_____

_____

_____

_____

_____

Generalize

10. The author concludes with the words "The future is yours to invent." What would you like to invent or see invented in the future? Describe how life would change if this invention became part of your daily life.

_____

_____

_____

_____

_____

_____

_____

_____

Vocabulary

Practise

Complete the sentences with words from the word bank.

Word Bank		
• apathetic	• gut	• tried and true
• acclaimed	• hedonist	• urges
• doodling	• quick-fix society	
• gregarious	• satyr	

1. The logo Fiorucci designed of the laughing _____ had little red horns on its head.

2. If Fabien had listened to his _____ he would have gone backpacking in Asia for a year, instead of failing his first year of university.

3. Some people blame our _____ for everything from high divorce rates to plastic surgery.

4. By the end of this decade, even the most _____ teens will have become more passionate about environmental issues.

5. It's confusing when you feel conflicting _____ about how to plan your future.

6. Haiyan told the company that her idea for the invention came to her as she was

   _____ on a pad of paper.

7. Your comfortable, _____ ways of doing things can sometimes prevent you from making exciting discoveries.

8. No one ever thought the shiest girl in drama class would one day become an

   _____ actress in Hollywood.

9. It was clear that Jim Carrey would become a comedian one day: His enthusiastic

   and _____ nature often disrupted classes.

10. The fashion designer is a self-proclaimed _____ who enjoys the lifestyle of the rich and famous on the Mediterranean.

Learn More

Complete each sentence with the correct word.

1. Ms. Dancause was proud to receive the _____ for her contribution to the company.

    a) scholarship   **b)** income   **c)** achievement award

2. If we had moved to the _____ of Vancouver, it would have been hard to cycle downtown to work.

    a) corporate world   **b)** housing development   **c)** suburbs

3. Do you think _____ will have a damaging effect on the young singer?

    a) high school sweetheart   **b)** fame   **c)** childhood

4. Many graduate students applied for the _____ to pay for their post-graduate studies.

    a) scholarship   **b)** training   **c)** investments

5. It was a real _____ when Réjean finally landed a major contract and was able to get his company off the ground.

    a) happiness   **b)** breakthrough   **c)** training

6. Will we have found _____ in making money and buying fancy cars and houses when we're older?

    a) fulfillment   **b)** leisure   **c)** relationships

Your Turn

What is the most important to you: happiness, fame, fulfillment, or relationships? Write a short text using at least five new words you learned in this unit to explain the kind of life you imagine you will have built for yourself in your thirties. Underline the new words. Support your answer with examples.

_____

_____

_____

_____

_____

_____

_____

_____

WORKSHOPS

The aim of this workshop is to help you learn how to write an opinion paragraph. An opinion is a statement of belief or an expression of a judgment you have formed, and it can be expressed in many different ways. It is important to know how to share your opinion effectively and convincingly. Remember: your opinion counts.

In this workshop you will learn how to:

- write a topic sentence to present your opinion and state your main idea
- provide reasons to support your opinion
- conclude your paragraph

The aim of this workshop is to help you learn how to write a descriptive text. When you write a description, you use words that help your audience see, hear, feel, taste and smell the things being described. A good description can make the reader feel like he or she is really part of the experience.

In this workshop you will learn how to:

- use descriptive language correctly
- write an introduction to present your topic and state your main idea
- write a development paragraph to show what something or someone is like
- write a conclusion for your text

The aim of this workshop is to help you learn how to write a biography. A biography is the story of a person's life. You can write a biography about a celebrity, a historical figure or someone you know personally. A biography can be a short paragraph or a longer text.

In this workshop you will learn how to:

- write an introduction about the subject of your biography
- write three development paragraphs presenting different aspects of the person's life
- write a conclusion for your biography

SECTION 2

Write an Opinion Paragraph

Grammar

Punctuation and Capitalization

Punctuation

Punctuation marks have different uses in written texts.

Punctuation Mark	Uses	Examples
Period (.)	• To end a sentence	*I lost my cellphone.*
Exclamation mark (!)	• To show surprise or emotion	*That's crazy!*
Question mark (?)	• To ask a question	*What do you think?*
Comma (,)	• To separate items in a list • Before or within a quotation • To separate clauses • To separate parts of a date	*voice mail, texting, email* *"Let's go," said Vipa.* *If they show up, call me.* *Monday, November 8, 2010*
Apostrophe (')	• To show possession • To indicate a missing letter or letters in a contraction	*Oleg's MP3 player* *Don't we have to hurry if we're going to catch our flight?*
Parentheses (( ))	• To add information or examples	*The simple tenses (present, past and future) are easy to learn.*
Colon (:)	• To introduce a list • To introduce an explanation or summary of information	*Everyone's here: Juan, Phil and Alek.* *The message is clear: be punctual!*
Quotation marks (" ")	• To indicate direct speech	*"How long did you chat last night?" Wanda asked.*

Capitalization

Uses	Examples
Capitalize the first word of every sentence.	*Remember to log out of your email account.*
Capitalize most words in titles and subtitles of works.	*Interview With a Vampire* *Canadian Oxford Dictionary*
Capitalize proper nouns (persons, organizations, geographical names, days of the week, months, holidays).	*The House of Commons will be in session in Ottawa starting on the first Monday in October and until the Christmas holidays.*
Capitalize proper names, races, nationalities and languages.	*Kevin is Taiwanese, but he speaks excellent English and French.*

→

Uses	Examples
Capitalize adjectives and common nouns used as essential parts of proper nouns.	*The National Gallery* *The First World War*
Capitalize trade names.	*Blackberry, Ipod, Koolaid*

Frequent Errors

The sentences below contain errors in punctuation or capitalization. Rewrite them correctly. Some sentences may contain more than one error.

1. Teenager's today spend too much time using media devices.

_____

2. Advertisements in Teen Magazines send the wrong message to young people.

_____

_____

3. Most adults have forgotten what (it was like) to be young!

_____

4. Education, isnt a priority for teens today.

_____

5. Professional athletes like nhl players are underworked and: overpaid.

_____

6. Teens learn better now because they use technology like the Internet, and email?

_____

_____

7. All students should learn a third language like spanish or german.

_____

8. Its rude: to talk loudly on your cellphone, on the bus said Ricky.

_____

9. The crazy challenges and, fast pace make the amazing race the best reality tv show.

_____

_____

10. Working after school is'nt the best idea if you're failing classes'?

_____

Practise

Read the paragraph below. Complete the text using the correct punctuation and capitalization.

Using cellphones, playing video games listening to portable music devices, sending emails, instant messaging, social networking you name it, today s teens are doing it Studies show that some teens spend up to 72 hours per week using electronic devices That s almost twice as many hours as someone working a full-time job As a result, more time is devoted to media use than to other activities such as sports and exercise. Is it any wonder therefore that childhood obesity is on the rise Teenager catherine benham says, We need to take action and get canada s youth on the move again. Otherwise, our future doesn t look very bright

The Opinion Paragraph

You share your opinion when you:

- participate in class discussions
- discuss issues with your friends and family
- contribute to a blog
- write a formal text in response to a story or poem you read in school
- respond to an article in your local newspaper concerning an issue that you feel strongly about

A. Model of an Opinion Paragraph

Understanding the features of an opinion paragraph.

Text A

Title
Predicts what this text will be about.

Topic sentence
Presents your opinion on the subject.

Supporting points
The topic sentence is supported with examples, comparisons, facts, personal experiences or anecdotes.

Conclusion
Restates the topic sentence and ends the paragraph with a recommendation or a closing statement.

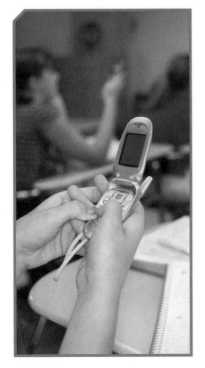

Leave It in Your Locker

You're sitting in class when you hear the unmistakable buzz of a vibrating cellphone. You look around to see a few nervous faces and some hands reaching into pockets. Cellphone use in class is the subject of discussion in many high schools around the world. Some argue that cellphones should not be allowed in schools at all. Others claim that they are acceptable as long as students don't use them during school hours. I don't think we can prevent students from bringing media devices to school but in my opinion, cellphones do not belong in the classroom. First of all, the temptation to text a friend while the teacher's back is turned is very hard to resist and even though we teens of the 21st century are known for our multi-tasking abilities, any attention devoted to a text message is attention taken away from the lesson. Secondly, I don't think that anything is so important that it can't wait until after class. Texting your girlfriend to arrange your lunch date at the cafeteria might seem urgent but I'm sure it can wait until the break. In case of a true emergency, our parents can contact us through the secretary or the principal. Finally, I know that some students use their cellphones to engage in behaviour that has absolutely no place in the classroom or in the school at all. Banning the use of cellphones in class won't eliminate the problem but it reduces the time students have to plan undesirable activities. Let's focus on learning and leave our cellphones in our lockers where they belong.

Text B

Title Predicts what this text will be about.
Topic sentence Presents your opinion on the subject.
Supporting points The topic sentence is supported with examples, reasons, comparisons, facts, personal experiences or anecdotes.
Conclusion Restates the topic sentence and ends the paragraph with a recommendation or a closing statement.

Junk's Out!

If you want a chocolate bar for a quick fix before last period, don't expect to buy it from your school vending machine. Québec schools have recently adopted new policies concerning health and nutrition. Cafeteria menus now offer healthier choices and vending machines have been emptied of chips and candy. All this is because childhood obesity is on the rise. According to statistics, approximately 25 per cent of Canadian children are overweight. Drastic figures call for drastic measures. However, I don't think banning junk food in schools is the answer. Eliminating junk food won't solve the problem. It's like forbidding children to use the Internet because of the potential risks. The dangers won't disappear and if children aren't taught how to respond to them, they'll be no safer than before. I believe that education is the key. Inform children of the dangers of a poor diet and the benefits of healthy eating and they'll use the information to act responsibly. Besides, an occasional chocolate bar does no harm. I'm all for promoting healthy eating but moderation is the key. Something that's forbidden is much more desirable! Encourage students to replace chocolate bars with nutritious granola bars, or chips with rice cakes. Teach them how to make the right choices and then we'll see some results. Furthermore, healthy eating is not the only way to achieve a healthier lifestyle. Physical activity is equally important. Schools should give us extra time for physical education or allow us to move about more during the day. We can't even get up to sharpen our pencils! Teach children to weigh the pros and cons of the choices they make each day and leave some treats in the vending machines so we get some exercise on the way to buy our candy.

Explore the Text

Before Reading

1. Read the titles of the two model texts on pages 113–114 and look at the photos. Predict what each text will be about.

   Text A: _____

   Text B: _____

2. Learn about the features of an opinion paragraph. Read the information in the margin beside each text.

While Reading

3. Read the two texts. Identify and highlight the following features:
   - the topic sentence: highlight in yellow
   - three supporting points: highlight in green
   - the concluding sentence: highlight in blue

After Reading

4. Answer the following questions about the two texts.

	Text A	Text B
a) Who wrote this text? Underline words or phrases in the text that helped you decide.		
b) For whom is this text intended? Circle words or phrases in the text that helped you decide.		

Connect With the Text

5. Choose one of the two texts. Decide whether you agree or disagree with the opinions and arguments presented in the text. Write a short paragraph in response. State your opinion and provide reasons to support your ideas.

   _____

   _____

   _____

   _____

B. How to Write an Opinion Paragraph

What?

In an opinion paragraph, you share your ideas and point of view on a particular topic. You state what you believe about something and defend it with valid arguments.

How?

1. Think about the topic you chose.

2. Think about the people who will read your paragraph. Choose your audience.

3. Brainstorm ideas about your topic and then develop your ideas to create an effective paragraph.

   • Write a topic sentence stating your opinion.

   • Think about how you will support your opinion: You can use examples, facts or statistics. You can also make comparisons. If you present information as fact, make sure you have proof that the statement is true. You can also draw on your own experience and share personal anecdotes to make your point.

   • Think about how you will conclude your paragraph. Restate your opinion and then provide a recommendation or conclude with a strong closing statement.

1. Your Topic

Read the list of topics and put a checkmark beside the ones that interest you. Select one topic to write about in your opinion paragraph.

Teenagers and media use	☐	Part-time work and full-time study	☐
Advertisements in teen magazines	☐	Childhood obesity	☐
Young people and education	☐	Learning a third language	☐
Professional athletes' salaries	☐	Reality TV	☐

2. Your Audience

Think about the topic you chose and decide who your audience will be.

_____

3. Your Ideas: Brainstorm

Think about the topic you chose in Step 1 and your targeted audience. Brainstorm your ideas using the graphic organizer for help. You can write your ideas in point form. The model below will help you.

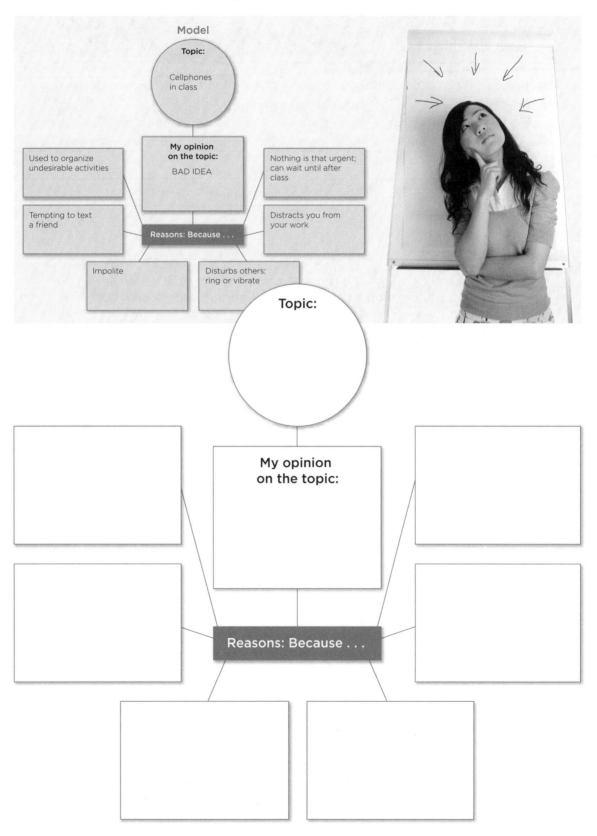

Model

Topic:

Cellphones in class

My opinion on the topic:

BAD IDEA

Used to organize undesirable activities

Nothing is that urgent; can wait until after class

Tempting to text a friend

Distracts you from your work

Reasons: Because . . .

Impolite

Disturbs others: ring or vibrate

Topic:

My opinion on the topic:

Reasons: Because . . .

4. The Topic Sentence

> The first step in writing an effective paragraph is a **well-written topic sentence**. The topic sentence presents the main idea of your paragraph. All other sentences in the paragraph relate to this one. The topic sentence is usually found near the beginning of the paragraph but can also be placed in the middle or at the end. In an opinion paragraph, the topic sentence presents your opinion on the subject.

Practise writing a topic sentence for your opinion paragraph. Refer to the topic sentences in Frequent Errors on page 111 for models and ideas. Remember to use correct punctuation and capitalization.

_____

_____

_____

5. Develop Your Ideas

> Writing a solid paragraph is the foundation for writing a solid essay. Once you understand how to **develop a well-structured paragraph**, you can apply what you have learned to help you write a longer text. Every sentence in the paragraph must relate to the topic sentence. Present your ideas in a logical order. In an opinion paragraph, present your arguments from strong to strongest. Support your arguments.

A. Select three reasons to support your opinion. For each reason, find supporting information. Remember to use examples, facts, statistics, comparisons, anecdotes and personal experiences. You can write your ideas in point form.

Reason 1:

Supporting information:
-
-
-

Reason 2:

Supporting information:
-
-
-

Reason 3:

Supporting information:
-
-
-

B. Using the notes you took on page 117, combine your ideas to write sentences that will be the body of your paragraph.

- Write at least three sentences. Present your reasons and supporting information.

- Rate your ideas from strong to strongest.

- Decide on the order in which you will present the ideas in your text.

1. _____

_____

_____

_____

_____

2. _____

_____

_____

_____

_____

3. _____

_____

_____

_____

_____

6. The Conclusion

An effective paragraph **ends strongly** and leaves the reader with something to think about. In the conclusion, you restate the topic sentence using different words. In an opinion paragraph, you restate your opinion and then end with a recommendation for action or with a strong closing statement.

Practise writing a strong conclusion for your paragraph.

_____

_____

_____

_____

_____

C. Write Your Opinion Paragraph

1. Write Your First Draft

Use the information from the practice activities to write the first draft of your opinion paragraph on a sheet of paper. Revise and edit your text using the checklist below.

✓	Checklist
	I wrote a topic sentence for my paragraph.
	My topic sentence clearly presents my opinion.
	I included at least three reasons to support my opinion and supported each one with concrete details and examples.
	I placed my paragraphs in a logical and effective way.
	I wrote a concluding sentence for my paragraph.
	I restated my opinion in the concluding sentence.
	I wrote a captivating title that is inviting to the reader.
	I used only complete sentences in my paragraph.
	Each sentence begins with a capital letter and ends with the appropriate punctuation.
	I used transition words to help my ideas flow smoothly.

2. Write Your Final Draft

Write the final draft of your opinion paragraph on a sheet of paper. Refer to the checklist again, if necessary.

3. Publish

- Post your opinion paragraph on the class bulletin board or the school website.
- Read some of your classmates' texts. Give them feedback on their ideas. Write your comments on sticky notes and post them on the texts. Comment on your classmates' choice of topics, the opinions presented in the paragraphs and the supporting arguments.

Write a Descriptive Text

Grammar

Qualitative Adjectives

- You use adjectives to modify (describe) nouns and pronouns. **Qualitative adjectives** (*enormous, young, oval, green, wooden*) provide information about the size, age, shape, colour, origin, material or purpose of a person, creature or thing.

  The floating market was reflected in the glassy green surface of the river.

- Qualitative adjectives usually appear before the noun and after verbs like *to be, to seem, to become* or *to get*.

  *Roland is such a **talented** artist.*
                  (adjective) (noun)

  *Roland is **talented**.*   or   *Roland seemed **happy**.*
  (noun)   (adjective)   (verb) (adjective)

- Qualitative adjectives always remain the same. They do not change to indicate number (singular or plural) or gender (feminine or masculine): *a **smart** boy, a **smart** girl, **smart** kids*. The exception to that rule are the demonstrative adjectives: **this** and **that** change to **these** and **those**.

- Most adjectives do not have a special form. But there are some endings that we add to other words to form adjectives.

  *a sal**ty** cracker*   *a help**ful** guide*   *glob**al** warming*

- You can use several adjectives to modify a noun but it is generally best to use no more than three adjectives. Qualitative adjectives usually follow this order.

Order of adjectives	Examples			
1. attitude/emotion	*boring*	*funny*	*pleasant*	*pretty*
2. size/weight	*small*	*large*	*heavy*	*medium*
3. age	*mature*	*young*	*new*	*ancient*
4. shape	*oval*	*triangular*	*round*	*rectangular*
5. colour	*crimson*	*green*	*mauve*	*pale*
6. origin	*French*	*English*	*Vietnamese*	*Moroccan*
7. material	*silk*	*stone*	*wooden*	*plastic*
8. purpose	*digital*	*underwater*	*walking*	*technological*

*I wore my **new black leather** jacket today.*
             (age)(colour)(material)(noun)

*The **ancient Incan** ruins are described in this guide book.*
      (age)   (origin)(noun)

*Where is that **fantastic small silver underwater** camera?*
            (attitude) (size) (colour) (purpose)

→ LEARN MORE

- When you use two **adjectives of colour** to modify a noun, separate the adjectives with *and*. When you use more than two, use a comma between the first items and the word *and* before the final adjective.

  *The black **and** white illustration was beautiful.*

  *They found the orange, yellow **and** green scarf in the snow.*

- When you use two or more **adjectives in sequence**, only use a comma if the adjectives are of the same importance and can be used in any order. If you are not sure, replace the comma with the word *and*. If the sentence still makes sense, you should use a comma.

  Correct: *The **ugly beige** car was parked outside our house.*

  Incorrect: *The ugly and beige car was parked outside our house.*

  Incorrect: *The ugly, beige car was parked outside our house.*

  Correct: *The frightened and lonely boy cried for his mother.*

  Correct: *The **frightened, lonely** boy cried for his mother.*

  Correct: *The **lonely, frightened** boy cried for his mother.*

Frequent Errors

The sentences below contain errors in adjective placement. Underline the adjectives in each sentence and use the information in the grammar box to help you correct the order.

1. The Canadian excited young audience cheered until the band played an encore.

   _____

   _____

2. I stuffed my books into my brown old canvas schoolbag.

   _____

3. The science teacher is a new refreshing addition to the school staff.

   _____

4. We always go to that Italian amazing small restaurant for my birthday.

   _____

5. The walking ultra-light Japanese shoes are on sale.

   _____

6. The surgeon always changes into her loose cotton grey sweatpants after work.

   _____

Practise

Think about some people, animals, places or objects. Write them in the first column of the table. Find four adjectives to describe each one and complete the table.

Noun	Adjective			
1.				
2.				
3.				
4.				
5.				

Write a sentence to describe each noun using three adjectives from the chart above. Place the adjectives in the right order.

1. _____

2. _____

3. _____

4. _____

5. _____

The Descriptive Text

Descriptions help you develop and expand on ideas in many types of texts and when you talk about everyday situations. You use descriptive language when you:

- talk or write about characters and settings in stories you read in class
- write your own short story or play
- write a poem about a particular person, animal, place, object or event
- share details about a personal experience with your family or friends
- relate a memory of something that happened to you

A. Model of a Descriptive Text

Understanding the features of a descriptive text.

Title
Predicts what this text will be about.

Introduction
Presents the topic and the thesis statement.

Thesis statement
Presents the main idea of the text.

Development paragraph
Provides a vivid description of the person, place, object or event.

Conclusion
Restates the thesis statement.

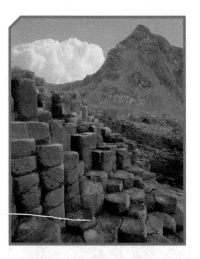

VOCABULARY

ebb and flow: fluctuation of the ocean

grazing: feeding on grass

gust: a blast of wind

jutted: stood out

lapped: splashed

screeching: making a harsh sound

speckled: dotted

Walking With Giants

It was a long, hard trek to the top of the cliff. The winding paths and uneven terrain presented a challenge for even the most experienced hikers. Surrounded by lush green fields speckled with fluffy white lambs, I stopped to massage my aching leg muscles, regretting my decision to hike all the way up the coastal route. I wished I was grazing in the meadows like the animals. But soon, there was no mistaking the scent of the ocean. I reached the top of the path and came face to face with the splendour of one of the world's most impressive landmarks: the Giant's Causeway. I had imagined many times what it would be like but nothing prepared me for the magnificent scene that lay before my eyes.

The rugged coastline was an amazing sight: 38 000 hexagonal grey basalt columns formed by volcanoes millions of years ago. Some of the columns jutted out from the sea, their heads raised high above the water. Others led directly into the treacherous ocean like stepping stones to a faraway land. It was easy to imagine legendary giants using the columns to cross the sea to another world. Strange rock formations surrounded me, each one offering a story. As the waves lapped against the rocky shore, their ebb and flow created a hypnotic effect, each rhythmic heartbeat luring me down toward the water. Although the sun was shining, a chilly sea breeze rose up, stinging my cheeks. A powerful gust almost pulled me off the rocks. I wrapped my jacket tightly around myself and held steady. The wind carried the scent of seaweed and tiny droplets of ocean spray, wetting my face. The burning salt on my lips was the taste of the sea.

The sound of the screeching seagulls as they swooped down toward the shore pulled me back to reality. It was time to return to the land and leave behind the mysteries of the ocean. I turned my back on the giants and their stories and started back down the winding path. I could almost hear the waves calling my name, urging me to always remember the spectacular sight imprinted on my mind that day.

Explore the Text

Before Reading

1. Read the title of the model text on page 124 and look at the photo. Predict what the text will be about.

_____

2. Learn about the features of a descriptive text. Read the information in the margin beside the text.

3. Scan the first paragraph on page 124 for the adjectives in the table below. Look at the noun that each one modifies. Guess the meaning of each adjective and complete the second column. Look up the words in a dictionary and write the definitions in the third column.

Word	What I think it means	What it means
impressive		
coastal		
lush		
fluffy		
winding		

While Reading

4. Read the text. Identify and highlight the following features:

- the thesis statement in the introduction and conclusion: highlight in yellow
- five descriptions in the development paragraph of what the author could see, hear, smell, taste and feel: highlight in green

After Reading

5. Find the adjectives in the text used to modify each of the nouns in the table below. Try to find at least two other adjectives that you could use to modify each noun.

Noun	Adjectives used in the text	Other ideas
trek		
terrain		
coastline		
columns		
rock formation		
shore		
beating		
gust		
seagull		

Connect With the Text

6. Can you imagine the scene that the author described? Which words or groups of words helped you feel as though you were there?

_____

_____

_____

_____

_____

_____

_____

_____

7. Think of a place you visited or a place that you like to be, for example your room, your favourite store or a faraway country. Imagine the scene in your head and then write down what you see.

_____

_____

_____

_____

_____

_____

_____

_____

_____

_____

B. How to Write a Descriptive Text

What?

In a descriptive text, you provide details about a specific person, place, object or event. The audience should be able to clearly imagine what you describe. Your description should also arouse the readers' emotions and make them feel as though they are part of the experience.

How?

1. Think about a person, place, object or event.
2. Think about the people who will read your text. Choose your audience.
3. Brainstorm ideas about your topic and then develop your ideas to create a three-paragraph text.
   • Write an introduction with a thesis statement to present the person, object, place or event you will describe.
   • Think about the descriptions you will provide in your development paragraph.
   • Think about how you will conclude your text. In your conclusion, you should restate your thesis statement.

1. Your Topic

Think about a person, place, object and event that you could write about in a descriptive text. Look at the photos on pages 122, 123 and 126 for ideas. Complete the graphic organizers with words or groups of words that come to mind when you think of each one. The model below will help you.

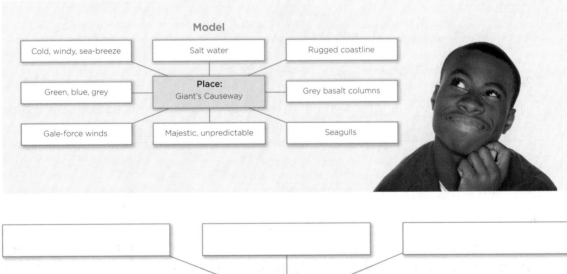

Model

Cold, windy, sea-breeze	Salt water	Rugged coastline
Green, blue, grey	**Place:** Giant's Causeway	Grey basalt columns
Gale-force winds	Majestic, unpredictable	Seagulls

Place:

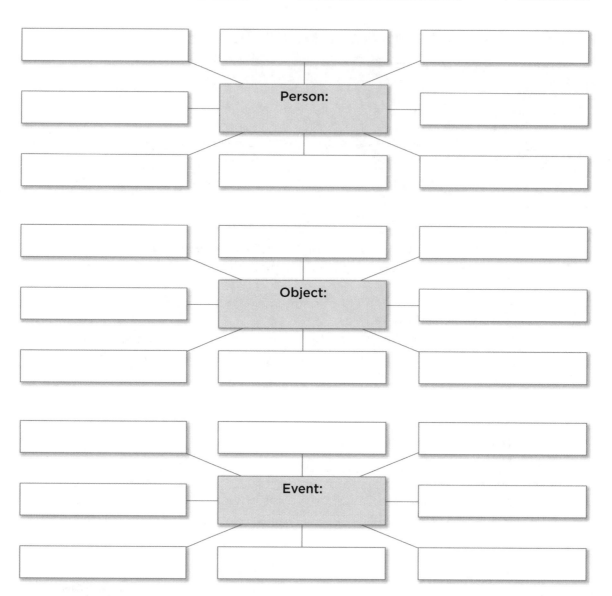

2. Your Audience

Think about one of the topics you chose and decide who your audience will be.

_____

3. Your Ideas: Brainstorm

Think about the topic you chose in Step 2 and your audience. Provide more details about your topic using the chart on page 129. Close your eyes and imagine the object, person, place or event. Write down what you hear, see, smell, taste and feel. You can write your ideas in point form. The model below will help you.

Topic: Giant's Causeway				
What I see	What I hear	What I taste	What I smell	What I feel
• waves • ocean	• seagulls screeching • waves hitting the rocks	• salt on my lips	• fresh ocean air • seaweed	• ocean spray wetting my face • cold sea air

Topic:				
What I see	**What I hear**	**What I taste**	**What I smell**	**What I feel**
_____	_____	_____	_____	_____
_____	_____	_____	_____	_____
_____	_____	_____	_____	_____
_____	_____	_____	_____	_____
_____	_____	_____	_____	_____
_____	_____	_____	_____	_____
_____	_____	_____	_____	_____
_____	_____	_____	_____	_____
_____	_____	_____	_____	_____

4. The Introduction

Read the sample introduction below. Highlight the thesis statement. Underline the person, place, object or event that you think will be described in the text.

One of my favourite activities is spending the day at an amusement park. I love to be in the hustle and bustle of people waiting to experience that unique mixture of terror and delight. Faces beam with excitement and the air is filled with happy shrieks and panicked screams. Last summer, I had the thrill of my life when I hopped on board one of the highest roller coasters in the country. The *Goliath* adventure was unlike anything I had ever experienced.

Think about what to include in the introduction to your descriptive text. Practise writing a thesis statement for your introduction. Refer to the sample introduction above and the text on page 124 for ideas.

_____

_____

_____

_____

_____

_____

_____

_____

5. Develop Your Ideas

A. Practise writing descriptive sentences about your topic. Write five sentences telling your audience about your topic. Then, think about how you can bring those sentences to life. Rewrite each sentence to show your audience what you mean. Remember to appeal to all five senses: sight, hearing, taste, touch and smell.

Telling	Showing	
1. _____ _____	_____ _____	☐
2. _____ _____	_____ _____	☐
3. _____ _____	_____ _____	☐
4. _____ _____	_____ _____	☐
5. _____ _____	_____ _____	☐

You can present the information in your development paragraph in different ways. You can use any of the following:

- Spatial order: describe where things are from your perspective or describe the object from top to bottom, bottom to top, left to right, etc.
- Chronological order: describe the events in the order in which they took place
- Order of importance: describe the event or object moving from the least important to most important characteristics

B. Read the five sentences you wrote in Section A. Decide on the order in which you will present the information in your development paragraph. Number the sentences from one to five in the order in which they will appear in your text.

6. The Conclusion

Read the sample conclusion below. Find and highlight the thesis statement.

The cheers and applause from the passengers gradually faded as each one relished the final moments of the ride. As the train pulled into the loading area and my heartbeat gradually stopped racing, I looked at the crowd waiting in line to get on the ride: their faces glowed with nervous anticipation. The train finally stopped and my safety harness popped open.

I stepped onto the platform, nauseous but happy, reliving every steel peak and valley of the spectacular ride. *Goliath* was indeed a giant of a roller coaster adventure.

Practise writing a conclusion for your text.

_____

_____

_____

_____

C. Write Your Descriptive Text

1. Write Your First Draft

Use the information from the practice activities to write the first draft of your descriptive text on a sheet of paper. Revise and edit your text using the checklist.

✓	Checklist
	I wrote an introduction for my descriptive text.
	I wrote a thesis statement that provides specific information about my topic.
	I wrote a development paragraph.
	I presented the details in my development paragraph in a logical, effective order.
	I wrote a conclusion for my text and restated my thesis.
	The description of my person, place, object or event is clear and easy to understand.
	I used adjectives to bring my text to life and wrote the adjectives in the correct order.
	I used a maximum of three adjectives to describe each noun.
	I checked my use of verb tenses.
	I used correct capitalization and punctuation.

2. Write Your Final Draft

Write the final draft of your descriptive text on a sheet of paper. Refer to the checklist again, if necessary.

3. Publish

- Read your text to a classmate. Listen to your classmate's text. Close your eyes and imagine what is being described.

- Answer the following questions about your classmate's text and share your feedback with her or him:
  - Can you imagine the person, place, object or event that is described?
  - Does the text contain descriptions that appeal to all five senses?
  - Did the author use rich vocabulary and a variety of adjectives?
  - Are the adjectives placed in the correct order?

Write a Biography

Grammar

Common Prefixes and Suffixes

Prefixes

You use **prefixes** before a word to add something to the meaning.

Prefix	Meaning	Example	Prefix	Meaning	Example
ab-	far from, against	*abnormal*	over-	too much	*overcrowded*
bi-	two	*bicycle*	re-	again	*rewrite*
co-	together	*co-write*	semi-	half	*semi-conscious*
de-	away, down	*derail*	sub-	below	*submarine*
dis-	negation	*dislike*	super-	big, more	*superhero*
homo-	similar, like	*homogenous*	trans-	across	*transcontinental*
in-, im-	not	*invalid, improper*	un-	not	*unhappy*
mis-	badly, wrongly	*misunderstood*	under-	too little, below	*underestimate*

Suffixes

You use **suffixes** at the end of a word to change the function of the word.

Noun Suffix	Meaning	Example
-er	person who performs an action	*painter*
-dom	position or condition of	*stardom*
-ism	belief, act	*racism*
-ist	one who supports a belief or performs an act	*artist*
-ity	quality, condition	*creativity*
-hood	situation of	*adulthood*
-ment	abstraction of	*amusement*
-ness	circumstances of	*happiness*
-tion	presentation of an act or activity	*exhibition*

Dali

Adjective/Adverb Suffix	Meaning	Example
-able, -ible	capable of	*comfortable, terrible*
-al	of, relating to	*cultural*
-ful	filled with, full of	*forgetful*
-ic, -ac	like, related to	*historic, maniac*
-ish	like, connected to, coming from	*boyish*
-ive	having the nature of	*expensive*
-less	without	*formless*
-ly	like	*lovingly*
-ward	in the direction of	*outward*
-y	having	*furry*

Verb Suffix	Meaning	Example
-ify	transform into, shape	*glorify*
-ize	perform an action	*criticize*

Frequent Errors

The paragraph below contains words or parts of words that need prefixes or suffixes for the paragraph to make sense. Choose the most appropriate prefixes and suffixes.

My brother is the most _____reliable person I know. Every time our parents go away, he has a huge party with his craz_____ friends from our neighbour_____ . They make a mess and _____form the house into a real disaster area. Then, the next day, he tries to make me help him clean up and minim_____ the damage. He must think I am his idiot_____ little brother. I get so _____patient when he tries to tell me what to do. It's _____respectful to treat me like a servant! He thinks he is respons_____ for me but it's totally the opposite. My brother can be really thought_____ sometimes!

Name: _____ Date: _____ Group: _____

Practise

Add a prefix or suffix (or both) to change the meaning of each of the words below. Choose the correct prefix and/or suffix to form a word that has the same meaning as the vocabulary words in the final column. Use your dictionary.

Word	Prefix or Suffix	New word	Meaning
1. weight			skinny
2. read			to read incorrectly
3. sweet			in a kind manner
4. work			colleague
5. child			to act in an immature fashion
6. home			in the direction of home
7. race			having parents of two different races

The Biography

In a biography, you provide factual information about someone and relate significant events in the person's life. You write a biography to:

- pay tribute to someone you admire
- inform your readers about an important historical figure
- share information about a person who has made a difference in the world
- present someone you know personally

Sir Winston Churchill

© Jock McDonald 1988

Rosa Parks

A. Model of a Biography

Understanding the features of a biography.

Title
Predicts what this text will be about.

Introduction
Presents the person featured in the biography and the thesis statement.

Thesis statement
Presents the main idea of the text.

Development paragraphs
Provide information about the person's life, career and accomplishments. Each paragraph contains a topic sentence.

Topic sentence
Presents the main idea of each paragraph.

Conclusion
Restates the thesis statement.

earned: got
fled: escaped from
grappling: trying to deal with
pursuing: continuing
ruthless: cruel
shelters: protection or refuges
spousal: having to do with marriage

A Story of Freedom

Over 400 years ago when Samuel de Champlain established a French colony in America, he acted as governor of New France. A governor rules a country or province in the name of the monarch. Today, the governor general is the representative of the Crown in Canada and carries out the roles and responsibilities that would be assumed by the Sovereign. In September 2005, Her Excellency the Right Honourable Michaëlle Jean was appointed governor general of Canada by Her Majesty Queen Elizabeth II.

As a little girl growing up in a country suffering under dictatorship, Michaëlle Jean never imagined where destiny would take her. Jean's childhood was not an easy one. She was born on September 6th, 1957 in Port au Prince, Haiti. Living under the dictatorial regime of François Duvalier, Jean's father was separated from his family for 30 years. In 1968, the family **fled** Haiti and arrived as refugees in Canada, settling in Thetford Mines. During those years, Jean experienced racism and was at times excluded by other children. As a young adult, Jean studied at the University of Montréal and **earned** a number of degrees in languages and literature. Fluent in five languages and teaching at the Faculty of Italian Studies from 1984 to 1986, Michaëlle Jean had already become an accomplished adult who could be proud of her personal achievements.

It was clear even at this time, however, that Michaëlle Jean would have an impact at a greater level. While **pursuing** her studies, Jean worked for eight years in **shelters** for abused women, defending the rights of victims of **spousal** violence. She also helped to establish emergency shelters for women in

abusive relationships in Québec and Canada. Michaëlle Jean then went on to become a highly-respected journalist at Radio Canada and CBC. She started her career in journalism in 1988, working as news anchor for a variety of programs in both English and French before eventually hosting her own show in 2004. As Jean's voice was heard in homes all across the country, she continued her charity work with victims of abuse.

Michaëlle Jean's appointment as governor general represented a significant moment in Canada's history. Jean was not the first woman to be appointed governor general. However, she was the first of Caribbean origin to hold such a position. While most people welcomed the idea of a young, Haitian-Canadian woman holding Canada's highest public office, her appointment met with resistance from some of Canada's political leaders. Some felt the choice to be inappropriate and voiced concerns regarding Jean's husband, French filmmaker Jean-Daniel Lafond, known for his films about Québec independence. Despite the controversy surrounding her appointment, Her Excellency the Right Honourable Michaëlle Jean took her place in Rideau Hall on September 27th, 2005, becoming Canada's 27th governor general.

The reality of a young refugee from Haiti holding Canada's highest public office is a true story of hope for future generations including Jean's own daughter, Marie-Éden, whom Jean and Lafond adopted from Haiti. In her installation speech in 2005, Jean said, "The story of that little girl, who watched her parents, her family, and her friends **grappling** with the horrors of a **ruthless** dictatorship, who became the woman standing before you today, is a lesson in learning to be free."

Explore the text

Before Reading

1. What do the root words *bio* and *graph* mean? Use your dictionary.

   bio: _____   graph: _____

2. Learn about the features of a biography. Read the information in the margin beside the text. What type of information do you expect to read in a biography?

   _____

   _____

   _____

3. What do you already know about Michaëlle Jean?

   _____

While Reading

4. Read the text. Identify and highlight the following features:

   - the thesis statement in the introduction and conclusion: highlight in yellow
   - the topic sentence in each of the development paragraphs: highlight in green

5. Scan the text and underline information related to the following aspects of Jean's life: name, date and place of birth, childhood, education, career, family life.

6. Find words in the text that contain a prefix or suffix. Choose ten words and write them below. Circle the prefix or suffix in each one.

   _____

   _____

   _____

After Reading

7. Complete the graphic organizer with information from the text.

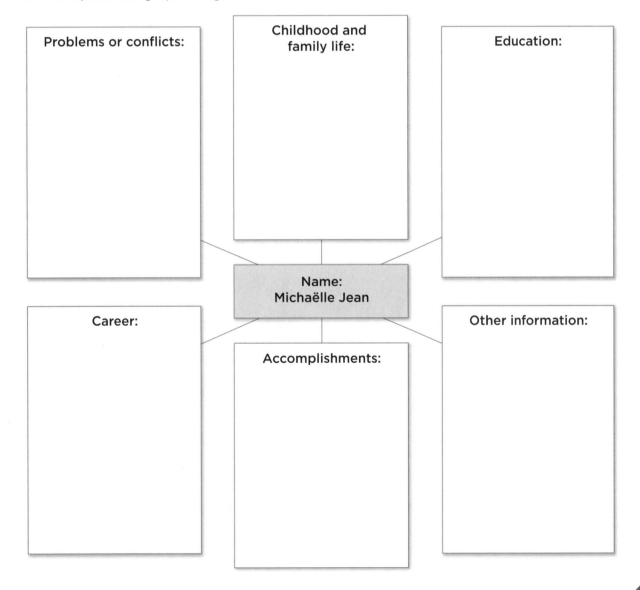

Problems or conflicts:

Childhood and family life:

Education:

Name: Michaëlle Jean

Career:

Accomplishments:

Other information:

Connect With the Text

8. Do you think Michaëlle Jean's biography explains why she is an important figure in today's society? Explain.

_____

_____

_____

_____

_____

B. How to Write a Biography

What?

In a biography, you provide details about a specific person. It is impossible to say everything about the person. You must decide what information you will include.

How?

1. Think about a person you would like to write about.

2. Think about the people who will read your text. Choose your audience.

3. Brainstorm ideas about the person you chose and then develop your ideas to write a five-paragraph text.

   • Write an introduction with a thesis statement to present the person.

   • Think about the information you will provide in your three development paragraphs.

   • Think about how you will conclude your text. In your conclusion, you should restate your thesis statement.

1. Your Topic

Think about the person you will write about in your text. Look at the photos on pages 132 and 134 for inspiration. You may choose to write about yourself: That is called an autobiography.

_____

2. Your Audience

Think about the person you chose and decide who your audience will be.

_____

_____

3. Your Ideas: Brainstorm

Complete the graphic organizer with information about the person you chose.
If you chose to write about an important historical figure or a famous person, you
will need to do some research. You can write your ideas in point form.

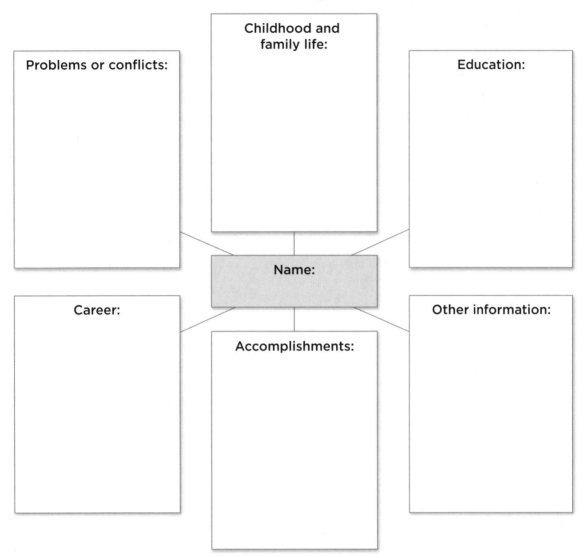

Childhood and family life:

Problems or conflicts:

Education:

Name:

Career:

Accomplishments:

Other information:

4. The Introduction

In this paragraph, you present the person that you will write about and the aspects
of his or her life that you will focus on. A **strong beginning** will attract your reader's
attention: Start with a quote from the person or a significant event in his or her life.

Think about the person you chose for your biography and the aspects of his or her
life that you will write about. Practise writing an introduction to your text. Refer to
the introduction to the text on page 135 for ideas.

_____

_____

_____

5. Develop and Organize Your Ideas

> In the development paragraphs, you **provide specific details** about your subject. Since your biography will include three development paragraphs, limit yourself to three categories of information.

A. Below you will find 12 facts about a famous political figure, Sir Winston Churchill. Read the information and group similar ideas together. Write the information in the columns of the table. Give each column a heading.

- Attended three schools
- Renowned politician and world leader who helped save the world from Nazi domination
- Did not do very well in school
- Enjoyed painting and baths
- One of the most influential people of the 20th century
- Prime Minister of Great Britain, 1940–1945 and 1951–1955

- Showed great strength as a wartime Prime Minister
- Trusted by nation
- Was not very close to father
- Won Nobel Prize in Literature in 1953
- Wrote a novel, biographies, histories of the two World Wars
- Born in 1874 to British father and American mother

Category:	Category:	Category:

B. Choose one category of information to practise writing a development paragraph. Write complete sentences and organize the details in a logical and effective way. Write your paragraph below.

_____

_____

_____

_____

_____

_____

_____

_____

_____

C. Look at the graphic organizer you prepared on page 139. Choose the three categories of information you will include in your text. Write them below.

Development Paragraph 1: _____

Development Paragraph 2: _____

Development Paragraph 3: _____

D. Decide on the order in which you will present the information in each development paragraph. In a biography, the information is usually presented in chronological order. In note form on the lines below, write the information in the order it will appear in your text. Use your resources to find more information for your text.

Development Paragraph 1:

- _____

- _____

- _____

Development Paragraph 2:

- _____

- _____

- _____

Development Paragraph 3:

- _____

- _____

- _____

E. Use the information in Step D to write a topic sentence for each of your development paragraphs and a transition sentence to connect one paragraph to the next.

Development Paragraph 1:

Topic sentence: _____

_____

Transition sentence: _____

_____

Development Paragraph 2:

Topic sentence: _____

_____

Transition sentence: _____

_____

Development Paragraph 3:

Topic sentence: _____

_____

Transition sentence: _____

_____

6. The Conclusion

> In the conclusion, you **sum up the information** about the subject of your text. Restate your thesis using different words. Emphasize the most important aspects of the person's life so your reader is left with a clear impression of the person and why he or she is worth remembering.

Practise writing a conclusion for your text.

_____

_____

_____

_____

_____

_____

_____

_____

C. Write Your Biography

1. Write Your First Draft

Use the information from the practice activities to write the first draft of your biography or autobiography on a sheet of paper. Revise and edit your text using the checklist below.

✓	Checklist
	I wrote an introduction for my biography that will grab my reader's attention.
	I wrote a thesis statement to present the person I will write about.
	I wrote three development paragraphs.
	Each development paragraph focuses on one aspect of the person's life.
	I presented the details in my development paragraphs in a logical, effective order.
	I wrote a conclusion for my text and restated my thesis.
	I checked my use of verb tenses.
	I used correct capitalization and punctuation.
	I checked all words containing prefixes and suffixes to make sure they are used correctly.
	I checked my spelling.

2. Write Your Final Draft

Write the final draft of your biography or autobiography on a sheet of paper. Think of an interesting title for your text. Refer to the checklist again, if necessary.

3. Publish

- Read your text to a classmate.

- Listen to your classmate's text.

- On a sheet of paper, draw a graphic organizer. Use the one on page 139 as a model. Complete the graphic organizer with information about the person featured in your classmate's biography.

Common Irregular Verbs

Base Form	Simple Past	Past Participle	Meaning
arise	arose	arisen	
awake	awoke	awoken	
be	was/were	been	
beat	beat	beaten	
become	became	become	
begin	began	begun	
behold	beheld	beheld	
bend	bent	bent	
bet	bet	bet	
bid	bid	bid	
bind	bound	bound	
bite	bit	bitten	
bleed	bled	bled	
blow	blew	blown	
break	broke	broken	
bring	brought	brought	
broadcast	broadcast	broadcast	
build	built	built	
burn	burned	burnt	
buy	bought	bought	
catch	caught	caught	
choose	chose	chosen	
cling	clung	clung	
come	came	come	
cost	cost	cost	
cut	cut	cut	
deal	dealt	dealt	
dig	dug	dug	
do	did	done	

Base Form	Simple Past	Past Participle	Meaning
draw	drew	drawn	
dream	dreamt/dreamed	dreamt/dreamed	
drink	drank	drunk	
drive	drove	driven	
eat	ate	eaten	
fall	fell	fallen	
feed	fed	fed	
feel	felt	felt	
fight	fought	fought	
find	found	found	
flee	fled	fled	
fling	flung	flung	
fly	flew	flown	
forbid	forbade	forbidden	
forget	forgot	forgotten	
forgive	forgave	forgiven	
freeze	froze	frozen	
get	got	got(ten)	
give	gave	given	
go	went	gone	
grind	ground	ground	
grow	grew	grown	
hang	hung	hung	
have	had	had	
hear	heard	heard	
hide	hid	hidden	
hit	hit	hit	
hold	held	held	
hurt	hurt	hurt	
keep	kept	kept	
kneel	knelt/kneeled	knelt/kneeled	
know	knew	known	
lay	laid	laid	

Base Form	Simple Past	Past Participle	Meaning
lead	led	led	
leap	leaped/leapt	leaped/leapt	
leave	left	left	
lend	lent	lent	
let	let	let	
lie	lay	lain	
light	lit/lighted	lit/lighted	
lose	lost	lost	
make	made	made	
mean	meant	meant	
meet	met	met	
pay	paid	paid	
put	put	put	
quit	quit	quit	
read	read	read	
ride	rode	ridden	
ring	rang	rung	
rise	rose	risen	
run	ran	run	
say	said	said	
see	saw	seen	
seek	sought	sought	
sell	sold	sold	
send	sent	sent	
set	set	set	
shake	shook	shaken	
shine	shone	shone	
shoot	shot	shot	
shrink	shrank	shrunk	
shut	shut	shut	
sing	sang	sung	
sink	sank	sunk	
sit	sat	sat	

Base Form	Simple Past	Past Participle	Meaning
sleep	slept	slept	
slide	slid	slid	
slit	slit	slit	
speak	spoke	spoken	
speed	sped/speeded	sped/speeded	
spend	spent	spent	
spin	spun	spun	
split	split	split	
spread	spread	spread	
spring	sprang	sprung	
stand	stood	stood	
steal	stole	stolen	
stick	stuck	stuck	
sting	stung	stung	
stink	stank	stunk	
strike	struck	struck	
swear	swore	sworn	
sweep	swept	swept	
swim	swam	swum	
swing	swung	swung	
take	took	taken	
teach	taught	taught	
tear	tore	torn	
tell	told	told	
think	thought	thought	
throw	threw	thrown	
understand	understood	understood	
undertake	undertook	undertaken	
wake	woke	woken	
wear	wore	worn	
weep	wept	wept	
win	won	won	
write	wrote	written	

→

Code	Description	Example
1. SV	Subject-verb agreement	(Ari ride) his bike every day. *SV*
2. SP	Spelling mistake	Alison is my favourite (cusin.) *SP*
3. CAP	Capitalize	I'll see you on (saturday) night. *CAP*
4. NO CAP	Do not capitalize	Do you like folk (Music?) NO CAP
5. WW	Wrong word	Safiya slipped and (blessed) her ankle. *WW*
6. ¶	New paragraph	When she finished writing her story, she was exhausted from working so hard on the ending. It was very late, so she went to bed. ¶ Tali's stepfather woke up early the next morning. He decided to surprise her with breakfast.
7. ⋏	Insert one or more words	My grandfather lives on ⋏ southern coast of France. *the*
8. —⸰	Delete	In five days, I will get my ~~my~~ driver's license.
9. #	Add a space	Did you enjoy the benefit#concert? *#*
10. ∼	Change order	Scott goes to the (School ∪ International.)
11. T	Wrong verb tense	Last year my family (go) to Morocco. *T*
12. rep	Avoid repetition	Then we went to the reading. (Then) we met the author. (Then) we asked her for her autograph. *rep*
13. P	Punctuation	What is the answer to question 2⸰ P
14. ?	Not clear	Denis is confused why his program not working next year. ?